The
Day
Jesus
Came To
Our
Town

RICHARD FEHR

A BULL'S-EYE  BOOK

Published by
William Mulvey Inc.
72 Park Street
New Canaan, Conn. 06840

Cover design: Ted Palmer

Library of Congress Cataloging-in-Publication Data

The Day Jesus Came To Our Town
"A Bull's-eye Book"

I. Title

PS3556.E38D3   1988   813'.54   86-90383

ISBN 0-934791-05-8

Printed in the United States of America

First Edition

The Day Jesus Came To Our Town was inspired in part by *In His Steps,* the enormously successful story by Charles Sheldon, written in 1896, which became a best-seller in many languages.

All Scriptural quotations are from the King James Version of the Bible.

June

1

Never before, at noon on a Friday, had Rev. Willard Merrill been so far behind on his Sunday sermon. The subject, notes and Bible references were usually well in hand on Friday. Then, Saturday could be devoted to developing the sermon.

Today—nothing had been done.

"Ann," the minister called to his wife, "what's happened this week? Two meetings yesterday, the problem with the building committee, the Devon funeral. And tonight there's a wedding rehearsal."

Ann, wearing a pale gray suit and bright pink blouse, descended the stairs. "I know, dear, your sermon." She put her arms around him. "The bazaar is tomorrow. We're setting up tables and decorating the room today. So you'll be alone here." She kissed him. She was a spirited woman, with long dark hair, a captivating smile and inquiring blue eyes.

Willard Merrill smiled. "I got a bit edgy this morning. Don't know why."

"Just don't answer the phone, dear. You're *always* on call. Promise?"

Willard Merrill nodded. He watched her leave and then sat behind his massive oak desk, the one the parishioners had given him four years ago on his fiftieth birthday, which coincided with the sixth anniversary of his arrival in Rockfort to become minister at the Pleasant Valley Church.

He soon selected 1 Peter 2:21 for his sermon. *For even hereunto were ye called; because Christ also suffered for us, leaving us an example, that you should follow his steps.*

He took a yellow pad and began to outline his sermon: the Atonement, Jesus' suffering in His life, His death; how we should try to follow Him, imitate Him in our lives. The doorbell rang. One short ring.

For a moment Willard Merrill didn't look up. There was his decision not to take calls. Those who came unannounced to the parsonage usually were children selling subscriptions or cookies. The usual solicitors passed up the Merrills. Apparently they felt the Pleasant Valley Church did its part in aiding the poor and comforting the sick.

The minister had risen from his red leather-covered swivel chair when the bell rang again. "All right!" Merrill shrugged and went to the front door. The parsonage was a two-story white frame house, resting on a fieldstone base about two feet high. The shutters were Williamsburg Blue and an attractive stone chimney dominated the west wall, facing the church itself.

The young man at the door was poorly dressed, just under six feet and painfully thin.

"Excuse me, sir. I'm looking for a job—anything. Being a minister and knowing a lot of people, I thought you might have an idea." His intent deep brown eyes seemed to pierce the screen. The minister pushed the aluminum door open and stepped out onto the porch.

"I'm afraid I—what sort of work do you do?"

"Steelworker. Last two jobs folded."

His gaunt face was a scratchy mass of dull black hair, the result of simply not shaving rather than an attempt to grow a beard. His lips were hidden by hair but his teeth were surprisingly white and even. "Know anybody at the truck terminal or food plants? They have signs up—no help needed. But I'll take anything."

Willard Merrill spoke softly. "Things are slow in Rockfort. We've been running over twelve percent unemployment. Have you tried the state employment office?"

2

"Yes." The young man looked away, his shoulders sagging slightly in discouragement.

"I wish I could help," the minister said. "I'd give you something here but we have nothing." He grasped the door handle. "I'm sorry, I'm very busy today. I do hope you find something."

Willard Merrill paused at a hall window to watch the visitor go down the walk to the street. The young man held a dark cap in his two hands, twisting it as if it were wet and he was trying to wring water out of it. His pace now was slow, dejected. For a moment he seemed to pause and sway a bit but the minister was certain the man was sober. Could he have been hungry? He was thin enough. Frowning, Merrill thought he might have offered food but it was too late now. The man was almost out of sight near the corner of Beech Lane.

Merrill returned to his study and in two hours the sermon was plotted; notes were neatly placed near the Bible, ready for his Saturday morning run-through.

He heard Ann returning and went out to meet her. She seemed brisker than usual.

"Janet and Sharon and I were arranging books and records to be sold tomorrow when the door opened and a man came right into the Activities Hall. Some sort of drifter. He just stood there. No one said anything. We were surprised to see a stranger barge in, such awful old ragged clothes. We were scared for a minute but he just sat down, without a word. Sharon said, 'Are you looking for someone?' I guess she couldn't think of anything else."

"Maybe he was tired, wanted to rest somewhere. The same man called here. Looked like a tramp?"

"Yes. Dirty and beat up. Like one of those bums you see in the movies. About thirty or thirty-three. In a minute or two, he suddenly got up and left without a word."

"Same man," Willard Merrill said thoughtfully. "I'm glad he was no problem."

"Finish your sermon, Will?"

3

"Yes. On the Atonement. And what we must do to follow Christ's example."

"I hope it doesn't rain again. We've had six bad weekends in a row."

Willard Merrill sighed. "Attendance has been down. With the weather—it's always easy to stay home." He stood in the hall without moving, lost in thought. Ann came over to him.

"Anything wrong?"

He shrugged. "No. I keep thinking about that young fellow. He seemed lost. Said he needed work, anything. If I'd really tried—"

"What could you do? Everything is slow. There you go, blaming yourself!" She put her hand on his arm. "Now forget about it, dear. He'll probably go to the Salvation Army."

The weather experts were wrong again. Sunday morning in Rockfort was beautiful. Clear, dry air. High fleecy clouds that seemed motionless. The Pleasant Valley Church was nearly filled before eleven, a congregation of well-dressed, affluent residents of the Pine Brook community that sprawled over several miles of rolling hill country. Lawyers, doctors, bankers, businessmen made up most of the congregation. Many were wealthy. Some were very wealthy, according to Willie Evans, the city tax clerk. Virginia Carver, with half the Carver real estate money, was the richest young single woman in Rockfort and one of the prettiest, too. Then there was Mrs. Austin Reese, with old General Motors money. And Hobart Varney, a retired oil tycoon.

The church was known for its fine music, and the organist and quartet choir were in excellent form this morning. To Willard Merrill, Marsha Hoyt's solo seemed appropriate for his sermon.

"Jesus, I my cross have taken,
All to leave and follow Thee.
Where He leads me I will follow.
I'll go with Him, with Him, all the way."

4

Marsha, in an off-white linen suit, was beautiful as she stood behind a low screen of oak carved with emblems of the cross and the crown. Her long auburn hair caught a shaft of light from one of the high stained glass windows, almost as if she was in a spotlight.

At 25, Marsha Hoyt was one of the most popular young women in the community. She often dated successful men but not any one steadily. And now, as her rich mezza soprano voice filled the church, the audience listened in enchantment. If applause was proper at the Pleasant Valley Church it would have been vigorous and extended.

Willard Merrill always drew inspiration from Marsha's solo preceding his sermon. Her performance set the stage for his delivery, like a fine overture. And the minister always rose to the occasion. Even critical Amy Gadsen admitted his sermons were wonderful. Parishioners liked what he said and the way he said it. They were people of means and accomplishment who enjoyed their preacher's forceful sermons.

Willard Merrill loved his work. He especially enjoyed his pulpit every Sunday, whether it was to experience the exhilaration of good attendance or to react sensitively to a small audience. He was never at his best on a stormy morning with a half-full church, but he forced himself on such occasions to think ahead to the promise of the following week.

Recently, he had felt as if his month's vacation each summer was too long to be away. Mid-way through today's sermon, he thought about vacation time. Only ten weeks and he'd be on his way to Maine. If Ann were not looking forward so eagerly—. He pressed on, using short sentences for emphasis, rising to his usual high dramatic level, but always stopping short of being overly dramatic. Good taste, scholarly interpretation and animation characterized Willard Merrill's sermons. He was a man with a compelling manner, tall, imposing, with close-cut iron-gray hair, steady blue eyes

5

and a strong, clear speaking voice. Some said he reminded them of Gregory Peck.

The minister looked directly at the audience for a few seconds after his final words. It was his way of adding emphasis to his message. He turned half of the large Bible over and moved to his chair to await the quartet's final selection.

> "All for Jesus, all for Jesus,
> All my beings' ransomed powers..."

Before the organist hit the first note it happened. From the rear of the church, from the shadows under the balcony, came a man's voice. "I've been sitting back here, wondering if I could say something at the close of your service." The man walked slowly down the aisle. The startled congregation turned. Willard Merrill knew at once who it was—the drifter who had come to the parsonage Friday morning. The man shuffled along, his gait uncertain. Twice he reached out to grasp the end of a pew for support. When he was directly in front of the pulpit he turned and faced the congregation.

"This is crazy. Don't know why any of you'd listen to me. But I might never get a chance again to sound off in a beautiful church like this. With all you nice people out there."

Willard Merrill took a step forward, as if to restrain the man. Then he stopped, studied the thin, stooped figure, the shabby, ragged clothes, the hands again twisting the well-worn cap. No one like this had ever entered the church, let alone had the audacity to address the audience. But somehow the stranger did not seem audacious. He was more a man who gently and firmly had a few words to say and assumed he would be heard, at least for a moment. His attitude, clearly, was: "What do I have to lose?" Then he spoke again. His voice was low but distinct. For a moment his manner reminded Merrill of a young divinity student he had once seen walking and talking in his sleep.

6

"I'm looking for a job. Been all over. I was a steelworker. You know what happened there. Then I got work on a newspaper delivery truck. Paper shut down. Too much television, they said. A lot of guys like me—mill hands—haven't worked at anything decent in a long time."

He paused and broke into a painful cough. Mrs. Oswald Yorke rose from her seat. He spoke again and she sat down. "Don't know anything but sheet steel. Roamed all over looking for a job to support my family." He looked down at the floor, as if he might be carefully choosing his next words. "They tell me I have to retrain for something. I want to do that. I'm young enough, not like all those guys in their fifties and sixties out there on the street."

He put up his hand to stay his audience, although no one had moved. "I was thinking, standing back there, if what you folks call following Jesus is the same as what He taught. He said, *Follow Me.* The good minister here said you have to follow in His steps. What steps? The reverend said 'obedience, faith, love and imitation.' What's that mean? How do you folks imitate Jesus? How do you follow Him?"

There was stirring now in the congregation. Some squirmed in their seats, looked at one another. Some wondered why Willard Merrill stood at his pulpit, said nothing. In the rear, two men rose and started to leave, then turned in the aisle and stopped to hear more.

The stranger stared at the audience in silence. There was a buzz of comments, a mixture of shock, indignation, bewilderment. "Well, I never—!" "Who *is* this person?" "Well, I don't intend to listen to—" Twenty-five or thirty were in the aisles now, shrugging, whispering.

"Three days around here looking for work. Didn't get a kind word. Except your minister here was kind. Didn't treat me like a bum. I know you folks can't pull jobs out of thin air, for people like me. But I wonder what you mean when you sing, 'I'll go with Him, with Him, all the way.'

Does that mean you help people, the way Jesus did?"

There was movement again in the aisles. More people began to leave. Mrs. Oswald Yorke, a large figure in a brilliant blue dress and a flowered, wide-brimmed hat, pushed past a group in the center aisle. She paused at the door as the young man spoke again.

"My wife died four months ago. Caught pneumonia in a Chicago tenement when the heat shut down. She didn't call help in time. I was hitchhiking back from a temporary job in Missouri." He seemed to have trouble going on. "She wouldn't go to a hospital and leave our little girl. When I got there, it was too late. Well...she's out of her trouble. My little girl's with folks I know in St. Louis until I get something steady. When I think about it, I get sort of confused at so many Christians living so good, singing 'Jesus, I my cross have taken, all to leave and follow Thee', and I remember how my wife died in a tenement suffering with fever and pain, crying to God to take our little girl, too. I know you folks can't stop dying—people all worn out and discouraged. You can't reach all over the world and help millions."

About half the congregation still remained. They had decided to hear the stranger out. Most stood in the aisles, a few were seated. "A church-goer owned that tenement where she died. The plumbing wouldn't work and you couldn't get heat in the winter. I wonder if he followed Jesus. 'Where He leads me I will follow. I'll go with Him, all the way.' Wouldn't there be a lot less trouble in the world if just a few folks who sing like that went out and lived those songs? There's people living in the streets, bus stations, parks. They stop looking for work. Can't look anymore. You get like that.

"You just wait, and die. No easy chairs, TV sets. You live for a day here, a day—and you just—"

Suddenly the stranger lurched forward, dropped the ragged cap and clutched at the end of the first pew. Gasps went through the audience. Willard Merrill moved quickly across the platform and down into the aisle. Dr. Les Egbert rose from his seat and was almost at the man's side. But it was too late.

The man lost his grip on the pew, fell heavily forward and lay motionless in the aisle, his face ashen white, his eyes closed.

2

At Benedict Hospital, where the stranger had been taken by West Rockfort First Aid, Reverend Merrill and Marsha Hoyt joined Dr. Egbert in a small waiting area on the third floor. Dr. Egbert had accompanied First Aid on the trip from the church.

For nearly an hour after the incident, the excitement and confusion of the young man's sudden collapse had kept Merrill busy at the church. Babbling parishioners milled about, airing opinions and offering advice. Janet Lauder said the stranger was mentally disturbed. "It's clear to me, he's *very* far off center. Because of his troubles and lack of proper nutrition. That man is not right."

Far gloomier was Mrs. Oswald Yorke. "He shouldn't be running around loose. With the kind of things that go on today, who knows what a man like that might do? It's just not safe to ignore these dregs of society. Where are the police?"

"I don't think the man's dangerous," Ann Merrill said. "He's just down on his luck and bitter about things. After all, he didn't ask for anything. He didn't threaten anybody."

"Well, I should hope not!" Mrs. Yorke replied and flounced off.

Willard Merrill nudged the group along, saying he wanted to get to the hospital. When he was about to get into his car, he saw Marsha Hoyt waiting at the curb. "Please ride with me, Willard. I'd like to talk with you."

9

It was a five-minute drive to the hospital. "I'm sure Mother will agree to this," Marsha said, her hands tensely gripping the wheel of her car. "I'd like to take this man in for a week or so. He could have the garage apartment. Give him a chance to get on his feet. Maybe if we all really tried we could find something for him to do. He needs some good food." At a red light, she looked at the minister, her eyes steady, her mouth set determinedly, awaiting his reply.

"That's wonderful of you. I imagine he'd jump at the chance, but then you never know. He seems to have a good deal of pride." Merrill paused. "There'd be an element of risk. We know nothing about the man."

"It's a chance we'll take." Her voice changed, reflecting deep concern. "If only one of us had been able to do something. Some money, a temporary job, anything. He seems so forlorn and sad."

Merrill again silently pictured the thin, bedraggled figure walking slowly from the rectory. And again he asked himself why he had not offered food. It's so easy to get caught up in the day's work, to be too busy for a person in need.

Marsha pulled into the hospital lot. They took the elevator to the third floor. "Dr. Spelling says the fellow's critical," Les Egbert said. "Definite heart problem. They're doing another EKG now. Extreme irregularity. And signs of serious lung congestion. Obvious malnutrition."

Willard Merrill frowned. "Then he'll be here a while." He turned to Marsha. "And he'll need care when he's discharged."

"He'll get it!"

A door swung open and a short, middle-aged man in a white coat came up to Dr. Egbert. "We're doing all we can. If you're very quiet you can go in."

Dr. Egbert said, "You two go in. I'm going to call Don Longren. He's a good heart man."

Willard and Marsha entered the small, dimly lighted room where there were four beds. Only two were occupied. In a bed by the far wall, an old woman lay motionless, her eyes closed. In the first bed, the stranger was on his back, his head rolling from side to side. He appeared to have aged; his face seemed thinner, whiter. He was moaning and sobbing incoherently and trying to use his arms to loosen the webbing that was keeping him prone. Suddenly his voice broke into a high, almost hysterical scream and he tried to sit up.

A nurse came in and moved quickly to his side. "He'll have to be sedated again," she said and rushed out of the room.

"I'll get Dr. Egbert," Marsha said. She hurried out.

Merrill moved to the edge of the bed and put his arms around the man's shoulders, more to comfort than to restrain.

"Now, relax. God is with you. God is here in this room, right now. You're going to be better. You're not alone. We're with you."

"You've been good to me," the stranger whispered. "What Jesus would do."

Suddenly he shook violently. A wracking, convulsive tremor went through his body and it seemed that he'd break his bonds and fall to the floor. Willard Merrill held him as best he could. Then, as quickly as it had started, the convulsion ceased. The man slumped back and was still. Merrill held him tighter.

The stranger died in his arms.

3
———

His face ashen, the minister slowly sank to his knees.

"God, grant this unfortunate soul peace and everlasting life. Be with him now with Your strength and Your guidance. Gather this servant in Your arms and hold him in peace and eternal life."

Merrill's prayer was interrupted by the arrival of the nurse. She was quickly followed by Marsha and Dr. Egbert.

The doctor confirmed the young man's death. Marsha covered her face with her hands. "Why didn't we do something!" she sobbed.

11

"Before you got here," the nurse said, "he kept trying to say something. It was hard to make out. It sounded like Saint Lou…and Betts…he said it over and over. Then he became completely incoherent."

"That's probably his child," Merrill said "Staying with friends in St. Louis."

Merrill turned to Marsha and the doctor. "You go down to administration, make arrangements for the funeral. The church will be in charge. I'll join you shortly."

When they had left, the minister again kneeled beside the still figure. He prayed for help, for strength, for guidance. He prayed for forgiveness. How did I fail, dear Jesus? How was I so unconcerned with the plight of this stranger? On my very doorstep was an opportunity to help, to comfort, to guide. And I did nothing. Why did I not, on Friday morning, do as it is written in Matthew 25: 35, 36. *For I was an hungered, and ye gave me meat: I was thirsty, and ye gave me drink: I was a stranger, and ye took me in: Naked, and ye clothed me.*

I did nothing, I turned away, occupied only with my own problems. This stranger received no food, no drink, no comfort from me.

May God help me!

4

On Wednesday, after the funeral, Ann Merrill knocked on the door to the study and heard Willard's "Yes?"

"Will, I ran into Amy in the bank today. She's wondering why you didn't return her call." Ann walked slowly to the desk and put her hand on her husband's shoulders. "You didn't return Ellis Grayson's call either."

When he didn't speak, she sat in the arm chair and waited, her eyes searching his expressionless face for some clue to his strange silence.

"Why?"

Slowly, the minister looked up. "I don't know."

"You're taking this whole thing too much to heart, dear. For four days now you've scarcely spoken to me. You've shut yourself up as if there's been a terrible tragedy."

She paused and stared at him but he gave no sign that he'd heard. "I know it was very sad about the young man. It was a pity he had to go like that. Don't think I don't feel for him and for his little girl. I do."

He was still silent.

"You can't go on like this, Will. You have obligations, a job to do. You can't just brood..."

"I'm not."

"I don't know what you call it. You've come out for meals— skimpy ones—and for the service today. The rest of the time you've been in a jail of your own making."

"I've tried to think, to meditate..."

"Of course you have, dear. But you can't be a recluse. You have to go on living. No matter how many drifters come to town or how many suddenly die. You're Willard Merrill, pastor of the Pleasant Valley Church, with responsibilities." She paused and went half way to the door. She turned back to him. "You're also my husband. And I'm here to help you. Or have you forgotten?"

Ann Merrill closed the door more firmly than usual.

The minister rose and went to the picture window. He stared at the four red cedars on the slope extending down to Brook Road. He moved his shoulders up and down in a hunching movement as if, physically, he might cast off his inner turmoil.

Something had happened to Willard Merrill. What was it? Over and over, since Sunday, this question had obsessed him.

Often in his lifetime he had faced a crisis. He had always overcome and emerged triumphant. Now, he sensed something far more perilous. He was facing a baffling turning point,

13

a puzzling crossroad, and for the first time he could not select the right course, a clear direction.

Standing there at the window, attempting to reach deep into his consciousness and pinpoint his dilemma, he realized he had always carried an emptiness, a questioning, a vague feeling of uncertainty and dissatisfaction. But so far it had not upset his life. He had moved ahead in his career as a minister and he had enjoyed a good marriage. His home had been all-important to him, a reflection of his own upbringing in a suburb of Cleveland where his childhood had been reasonably normal.

His father, C.G. Merrill, had been owner of a thriving wholesale grocery business, made to order, C.G. always said, for his only son.

"This idea of yours—being a preacher—is crazy. Here I am, at fifty, after working like a dog, wanting to spend a few years on the boat up at Mackinaw and you want to go off half-cocked with a Bible under your arm. I always figured you'd come into the business. I built it for you. The tough times are over. You got nothing to do but fill orders on time and keep the warehouse locked so they don't rob you, and enjoy life."

During Willard's junior and senior years at high school, his father's pleas grew in intensity, softened only by the quiet good sense expressed, usually at the dinner table, by Willard's mother. "The boy might as well do what he wants to do. You always did."

Soon after Willard decided to go to divinity school, his father sold out to a Chicago firm for a sum large enough to provide early retirement, a new boat and additions to the house in northern Michigan.

The next two years, mostly trouble-free, had rushed by. Merrill's ordination, an assignment as assistant to the minister of a church in Dayton; finally a chance to be appointed, near Zanesville, to a small church of his own. The next summer, during studies in Boston, he had spent a weekend at Wells

14

Beach, in Maine. And there, swimming in the ocean, with long rhythmic strokes, her bright red cap mostly submerged, had been Ann Gratton.

Their marriage the following winter signalled the true start of Willard's career. He took over a church in Illinois and became so well-liked that several parishioners actually cried the day Merrill announced he would be moving on to a larger community. Fifteen years later, Rockfort, Indiana, beckoned. It was by far the most prestigious assignment of all. Willard could not refuse. Ann was ecstatic. Not only was the Pleasant Valley Church magnificent, the parsonage was far more luxurious than anything the couple had ever occupied.

And the wealthy congregation was a challenge.

Willard Merrill knew he had to become a better speaker with a more incisive style than in the past. His audiences expected him to lead, to inspire, to teach, to be the strong central figure in the church and the community.

He plunged into his work, often studying the Bible until far into the night. He bought a tape recorder and worked on his voice levels, his inflections, dramatic pauses and all the little nuances so important in mastering conviction—the key to success in the pulpit.

How relatively easy it had been, he told himself now as he returned to his chair. Yes, he had worked hard. He had studied and sacrificed to reach his position in the church. But he had experienced no real problems. From the start it had been clear that the families in West Rockfort demanded something quite above the average but, when they got it, they were generous in their approval.

Was that Willard Merrill's goal? Approval? Was the approval of one's employers the ultimate measure of success? If so, then Merrill had reached his peak. That was enough.

Suddenly he reached out and slammed his right hand down on the desk. No! It was not enough! To simply ease through the motions? To coast through life? Was that all he needed to do? Many would say 'yes'.

15

His parishioners were content; they were highly pleased with their minister. They left church on Sunday, nodding and exchanging greetings, praising everything. They vowed to themselves to remember, to act, to change.

"A wonderful sermon." "Just what I needed to hear." "He's so clear and sensible." "I wish my daughter had heard that." "I said the same thing to John a few days ago."

One by one they'd file by at the door, shaking his hand and smiling, "Thank you, Reverend." "It was such a fine sermon." "Gives me something to think about I can tell you." "You said it all, and so well." "It was just thrilling!"

Then they went home and forgot all about the sermon.

Willard Merrill slowly rose from his chair. For the first time in his life he thought he saw the cause of his underlying doubt, his uneasiness, of the void that had lurked deep in his being. It was bland acceptance. Acceptance of worldly success as measured by popular standards. Acceptance of things as fine, as they are.

Each Sunday he adapted the teachings of Jesus to a format and presented them in a convenient package designed to awaken his listeners to their true selves, to bring them into patterns of behavior thought to be proper, just and humane. What else? He shook his head. Surely there was more than that.

He began to pace the floor. What am I, Willard Merrill, doing about myself? Am I living what I preach? Am I *really* living as Jesus intended me to live? If so, why, for the past few days, have I been in Hell?

Suddenly he knew. In spite of his success, his life was sadly incomplete. His existence was attuned to smugness and comfort; it was awash in satisfaction.

Willard Merrill was afraid. He knew he had to change. He was unable to go on as before. But how would he change? The church did not want him to change. The parishioners did not want him to be different. They wanted him to conform, to be the same tomorrow, next month, next year.

16

Ann certainly did not want him to change. She enjoyed her position, her activities and responsibilities. She was well-liked in West Rockfort. And it made her happy. Satisfaction was everywhere.

Willard Merrill knew that Jesus had not reached a point where He could relax in the satisfaction of His achievements. It is all too easy to be content, to relish our possessions, our strengths.

The minister reminded himself of Romans 15: 1. *We then that are strong ought to bear the infirmities of the weak, and not to please ourselves.*

But Merrill had looked the other way. He had conserved his own strength. He had failed to share. He stopped pacing and stared blankly without seeing. What would Jesus have done? On Friday morning, at eleven-thirty, would Jesus have said: "I'm sorry. I'm very busy today," and turned his back on the stranger and returned to his study? Of course not!

The minister looked at the antique brass ship's clock Ann's parents had given them on their first Christmas together. It was five o'clock. He realized three hours had passed since Ann left the study. There was not a sound in the house. Probably she had gone out.

He locked the door. Ann would return any moment and he needed more time. Somehow he had to find an answer—a new direction—before he could face a living soul, even his wife.

He moved the cushioned footstool he and Ann had found years ago in a thrift shop and placed it beside his desk.

As he kneeled in prayer he tried to examine his dilemma, to look squarely at the nature of his turmoil. What did Jesus want of him? What was expected of Willard Merrill and why had he not fulfilled his role? And—how could he live and act differently without bringing disappointment, even distress to others? That was the real core of his problem. He had to find the answer. He had to embark on an entirely new way of

17

life, and yet he could not leave the church; he could not be apart from his wife.

His body trembled as he knelt on the stool. He grasped the edge of the desk for support, clasped his hands and lowered his head.

I ask God in heaven for answers to these questions now engulfing my mind, my soul, my every thought. Give me the ability to see clearly those issues that now blind me so completely. God, show me the true Christian way. I seek only to follow Jesus, to do as He would have me do. I have been far afield. I have been lost in complacency, my days have been...

The minister paused. He opened his Bible to Deuteronomy 31: 6 and read aloud: *Be strong and of good courage, fear not, nor be afraid of them.* He was indeed afraid of them. For years he had feared to rock the boat, to disturb the peace of his congregation, to mar the easy comfort of his personal life. *For the Lord thy God, he it is that doth go with thee; he will not fail thee, nor forsake thee.*

Willard Merrill lifted his eyes heavenward. "Jesus, lead me now in right action. Lift me from the torment of doubt and uncertainty and from the hell of lost opportunities. I ask only for Divine guidance, for the clear and proper course.

You have said: *Ask and it will be given to you.* I now ask, Oh Lord, for thy help. Show me the way. I will follow Jesus.

Willard Merrill knelt in silence, his head on his hands, for a long time.

"Willard! Willard, are you in there, dear?"

5

Later on that same Wednesday Marsha found her mother in the sunroom, working on the final stages of a knitted scarf.

"The minute I saw you step out of your car, Marsha," Grace Hoyt said, "I knew you were upset over that boy." She

18

was a big woman, wearing thick horn-rimmed glasses and a pearl necklace.

Marsha sat in a cushioned wicker armchair. "I can't shake the feeling that all of us are to blame," she said. "There must be a way for people in real need to get help. We have the regular programs at the church. They're fine, as far as they go, but there must be something more."

"As long as the politicians keep avoiding our real problems we're going to have the poor and the sick and the unfortunate."

"We can't keep leaving everything to the government. What can I do? What can *we* do?" Marsha paused. "I didn't tell you this but I wanted to let that man stay in our apartment until he got on his feet."

"A street bum that nobody knows? How could you have imagined such a thing?"

"Mother, don't get excited..."

"I'm not excited. You're the one who's worked up over a drifter who has a heart attack and dies. Why, you weren't that concerned when your uncle Fred died!"

Eldon Hoyt's car entered the driveway and Marsha went to meet her father. He put his arm around her and they came back to the sunroom. After the usual greetings, Mrs. Hoyt said: "El, this girl is still upset about the stranger who died. You can't go into manic depression about someone you don't even know!" She shrugged and left the room.

"I'm sure it's not that bad," Eldon Hoyt said in the brisk manner that made his habitual optimism all the more forceful. "It was dramatic, all right. I bet very few churches ever have a drifter off the street walk right in and take over the pulpit."

Eldon Hoyt went over to a side table and poured two glasses of Canada Dry and added slices of fresh lime. He was a trim, quiet man.

"Do you think I'm wrong to be disturbed about what happened?" his daughter asked.

"You've always been a considerate person, Marsha.

19

Involved. I expect you to be that way." He carried the glasses to the coffee table, sat on the sofa and placed his feet on an ottoman. "How long have you been soloist?"

"Three years now."

"You get along well with Will Merrill. You're always pitching in. Thanksgiving, Christmas and all. Do you feel you ought to be doing more?"

She looked away, as if lost in thought. "There was something about this stranger. Maybe because I was right there, only a few feet from him. But when it was over, after he died, I felt terribly helpless. As if I could have rushed down into the aisle to keep him from falling. Crazy, isn't it?"

"No. Not at all."

Marsha sat next to her father on the sofa. He reached out and took his daughter's hand. They were silent.

The phone rang. It was Virginia Carver, Marsha's best friend. "Just got in from Chicago," Virginia said, "Can you come over? Have supper with me?"

Marsha looked at her father. "Do you mind if I...?"

"Go ahead. We're only having meat loaf."

He put down his glass, smiled. When she was at the door, he said: "You do what you think is right, dear."

"Thanks, Dad."

The Carver's handsome brick Georgian residence, Brooklawn, was one of the showplaces in the Storm Ridge section of West Rockfort. It was built in the Sixties by Alfred J. Carver, a multi-millionaire Chicago real estate developer, so his family could enjoy a small-city atmosphere. After his retirement in 1978, Mr. Carver continued to add to his wealth through wise investments in small companies in need of financing. Then he suffered a series of heart attacks.

In the year following her father's death, Virginia Carver was slow to emerge from her deep sorrow. For months she ventured out only for trips to Chicago connected with the estate and to attend services at the Pleasant Valley Church.

During this period, her father's sister, Geraldine "Deeny" Carver, had come to live at Brooklawn with Virginia and her older brother, Gerald.

Virginia and Marsha sat by the pool in the late afternoon sun. "What happened at the church?" Virginia asked. "Deeny told me a little but she wasn't too clear."

She sat back on the green chaise lounge, her long dark hair falling casually to her shoulders. Her dark blue eyes, alert and searching, reflected the confidence of great wealth. Virginia lacked for nothing. Cars, expensive clothes, a fine home, servants, the means to travel, an apartment in Chicago.

Virginia attracted men but made them feel uneasy. There was an aura about her. She was a person of depth, and men felt it. This held them at arms length. Growing up, at college and later, she had all the dates she wanted, but never a steady.

Some said that Virginia's wealth—it was estimated at around $30 million—kept many men off balance, and she was far too perceptive and mature to be taken in by fortune hunters.

Marsha told Virginia the story of the strange young man in the church, his remarks, collapse and eventual death in the hospital.

"He asked what we meant by following Jesus—that was the theme of Willard's sermon. He asked if things wouldn't be better in the world today if we imitated Jesus...rather than just sing about it in church."

Both were thoughtfully silent. Then Marsha said, "If one of us had been there Friday when he first appeared would we have helped him? With all our involvement, are we living as real Christians? What should we be doing? Following Jesus? How?"

Virginia Carver stared out beyond the pool, toward the broad sloping lawn with its magnificent oaks. There was a long silence before she spoke.

"Ever since Dad died, a question keeps recurring. What am I doing with my life? I'm busy all the time. I have everything. I'm happy. At least I think I'm happy. But what is the

21

real meaning of my life? How can I make it *more* meaning-ful? I'm searching for something. It has nothing to do with money or possessions. It's something deeper." She sighed and then her lips parted in a half smile. "It all comes down to one question, I guess. Why am I here?"

"That could explain *my* mood these last few days," Marsha said. "I'm determined to do something, something over and above anything I've done before. This business of the stranger has affected me somehow."

When Virginia did not answer, Marsha went on. "Here I am, singing and working for the church. I want to be doing more. But what?"

"I feel the same way."

"Take the young man's question—what would Jesus be doing in our situation?"

"That's a hard one."

"Let's talk to Willard. He'll have a suggestion. Maybe we can come up with a plan. A plan of some kind."

6

On Friday morning, after a restless night, Willard Merrill was alone in his study, kneeling in prayer as he had during most of the week. He had forced himself to look at his mail and answer incoming calls. Aside from that, he continued his struggle with the question: What does Jesus want of me?

To live as He would live, of course!

If only it could be that simple!

He rose, pale and shaken at the persistent answer that had pounded at him for three days: *To live as He would live!*

It was impossible. This is the twentieth century, in mid-America. This is the time of television, computers, satellites, miracle drugs. These are the days of strife in the Middle East, in Central America, of huge deficits, unemployment, on-again, off-again inflation. Wasn't it completely impractical to think of living today as Jesus would live? Yes. It was so totally at odds with present conditions. So abstract. So distant from reality. It was beyond all consideration.

Or was it?

Will Merrill, exhausted, stood at the window in the silence of his comfortable study and, slowly, a new question gripped him: *What else is there?* What else can possibly be important in my life except to do as He would do? Isn't that why He put me here? To do as He would do? Isn't that why He called me?

From his junior year in high school Willard Merrill had known that he'd become a minister. His friends in those days were headed for law school, medicine or retailing, but these fields held no interest for him. He wanted to make his life more meaningful.

Now, after twenty-eight years in the ministry, he was locked in a battle for his very survival. He was at a major crisis, a decisive point in his life, caught in a desperate conflict between his spiritual self and the practical world around him—his worldly self. What was it about the stranger's death—not an everyday death, but still an event that most would soon forget—to make Merrill question his own purpose in life?

Once again he made a brief appearance at dinner, apologized to Ann and retreated to his study at about eight o'clock. All through the night he struggled with himself. Why? What course? What decisions? How should he move? In what direction?

He paced incessantly. He read passages in the Bible. He prayed. He threw himself on the couch and attempted to sleep. It was impossible. Each time, he roused himself to pace and pray.

Finally, at five in the morning it happened. After six days of inner turmoil Willard Merrill suddenly was aware of a calmness, a sense of peace he had never known. Kneeling in prayer, his eyes were drawn heavenward. There, with great clarity, he saw a white glow of light. It broadened and then filled the room and went beyond. It seemed to fill his very being. It encompassed him completely—his body, mind and soul. He realized beyond all doubt that it was the Holy Spirit, descended to guide and direct his actions, his life.

After a time, Willard Merrill rose, his mind incredibly clear, his body imbued with a great new strength. Gone was all tension. Stress had vanished. His handsome face glowed with peace, serenity and confidence. His eyes shone with unshakeable determination. He knew what he had to do. And in knowing, he felt an all-encompassing peace unlike anything he had ever experienced. Instinctively, he was aware of what had happened.

He had been endowed with the power of the Holy Spirit.

His goal was clear. *He would follow Jesus!* He would do as He would do! It would not matter what obstacles might bar his way. No matter what others might say or do. All Willard Merrill's thoughts, all his actions, his entire life from this moment would be based on a single question.

What would Jesus do?

His course was irreversible. The details were far from specific. He had no clear thoughts of how he would proceed. But it didn't matter. All that would come. The basic idea was in place. Somehow, no matter what it took, he would do as Jesus would do. Not just in easy decisions, in lip service, but in every act, every thought. With God leading him, he would practice his new life, preach it, influence others to follow. He would begin at once!

Trembling with excitement, he sat at his desk and began to write his Sunday sermon, the most important he would ever give.

It was a sermon that was to change the world.

7

After dinner on Saturday, Ann Merrill served coffee in the living room.

"I'm so glad, dear, you've shaken off your concern over that man. It's the first time all week you've had a decent meal. You actually talked to me during dinner." She poured cream in her coffee and sat next to her husband. "You were in what my aunt in Maine used to call a blue funk."

"Ann, I have something to tell you."

"Yes?"

"This will sound odd to you, and I don't expect you to understand fully. Not at first anyway. But I'm starting a new life, a completely new life. I'm afraid it's going to mean some difficult adjustments." Ann Merrill's face clouded. She drew back on the sofa and regarded her husband questioningly. "I guess I've known for a long time," he continued. "I've realized something was missing."

She reached out to touch his arm. "It isn't…?"

"No, of course not. It isn't you if that's what you were going to say. We have a good marriage, Ann, and I love you. Our home life has been wonderful, and I've been lucky in my work. Moving here to Rockfort was the best thing we ever did."

"Well, then…"

"It's much deeper than that." He put down his coffee cup, rose and began to slowly pace the floor. It was as if moving would help him find the right words. "My life has been filled with so much. It's hard to imagine a minister with more to be thankful for. And, Ann, that's the real problem. Too much comfort. Too much ease. Too much of everything's-all-right. Coasting along. Doing a job. Receiving praise. Occupying a position of respect and approval in a fine community."

"I'm sure if they took a vote you'd be the most popular minister in Rockfort, and that includes James Graham."

"Ann, you could be right. But it's not enough. It's not what I'm here for. It's not my job to be the best in Rockfort, or second best, or any best, or worst."

He paused at the mantle, leaned on it and stared down into the fireplace. Ann Merrill sat up straight, her face a mask of bewilderment.

"My job," the Reverend Merrill said slowly, "is to do as Jesus would do. To follow Him. To live as He would live. And nothing less will do!"

She came over to him as he turned from the mantle.

"My dear, you're still upset over that man, I know it. Why, you're the most dedicated person I can think of. No one is closer to his work or to Bible teachings than Willard Merrill. You must stop blaming yourself for what happened last Sunday. It's ridiculous."

"From this moment on," he said firmly, "I intend to follow Him, in every detail, every thought, every action."

"That young man..."

"Jesus would not have turned him away. He would have taken him in. Fed him. Given him a place to rest. Helped him get back on his feet."

"You can't take in everyone from the street."

"Even Marsha was willing to have him stay in their garage apartment. It was too late. Everything was too late. It was too late by the time he walked into our church. *I* was too late."

"I can't believe you're this upset over what happened with... a stranger."

"It's not just that, Ann. Can't you see? The stranger was simply the incident, the event." He paused and looked at his wife. On his face there was both tenderness and concern. "I can't go on as before, I must do as Jesus would do, in every way, in every thought. I can't be just another minister, preaching a Sunday sermon. I wonder if you realize, if you have any idea at all, what it means to follow Jesus? Regardless of what might happen? If what He taught was right, then, it must be right today. The condition of the world means only one thing: We're not doing as Jesus taught us to do."

"You're a minister, practicing your religion. How do you intend to do as Jesus would do? You're already doing that."

"No. My work is just beginning."

"But how can you possibly do more than you're doing?

Your life is dedicated to the church, to your teachings, to your work. What is left? You can't suddenly become a saint and go around in strange clothes."

"I hadn't thought of doing that. What I'm going to propose tomorrow will be unsettling to some but I believe a few will join me. They will see the clear road ahead, the way of Jesus..."

"You mean your sermon will be about that?"

"Yes. It'll be exactly as I've tried to explain it to you, and I'll invite those in agreement to meet with me after the service."

"Of course they'll agree! It's easy to agree to anything. It's something else to really do it."

"I've thought of that."

"Willard. I think you should take more time. Don't rush into something you may be sorry for. Take another week or two and get your ideas organized. You can't expect people to suddenly go around all day blessing everyone they meet, smiling, helping old ladies cross the street and turning the other cheek at cheating, lying and rudeness."

"It'll be much more than that."

"More? Good heavens, what do you mean? Are they to come to church seven days a week?"

"No. They can do as Jesus would do if they never come to church."

Ann rose. With a degree of exasperation, she said: "Well, you do as you like. But don't be surprised at what they all say. Oh, maybe they won't come right out with it. Most are too polite for that. But they'll smile and whisper among themselves and as soon as they get home they'll be on the phone." She walked to the door, turned.

"They'll laugh, Willard. They'll laugh at you!"

8

Far into that night Willard Merrill prayed in his study. He prayed for guidance and the power to carry out his plan. As he knelt, his faith in his course of action soared and he experienced a new surge of energy. In the stillness he knew that what he was about to do was blessed with strength from the Holy Spirit. It was not Willard Merrill struggling to change but God the Father working in and with and through Willard Merrill, moving him forward with courage and conviction in the certainty of success.

He prayed through most of the night.

Sunday dawned clear and crisp, a perfect spring day. The Pleasant Valley Church was filled with a larger than usual turnout. Most knew that the stranger who had addressed the congregation had died. And word had gotten around that Reverend Merrill had been acting strangely.

It was no surprise, then, to see his drawn, haggard appearance as he took the pulpit. But his eyes were bright, his voice strong and he repeated the words from Matthew 10:38. *And he that taketh not his cross, and followeth after me, is not worthy of me.*

"Much that was said here last Sunday was a challenge to our ideas of Christianity. I have been studying…I might even say struggling…with definitions all week. What is our true role as Christians? What is *my* true role? Not only when I stand here before you on Sundays and on Wednesday evenings. But throughout each day. What is my job apart from my established duties as your pastor? If I'm a true Christian, I must be a true Christian all the time, in every action and every utterance every day. What *is* a true Christian? Isn't it a person who follows the teachings of Jesus? Who acts as He would act if He were in that person's place? Regardless of circumstances?"

Reverend Merrill paused. He looked over his audience and drew a deep breath as he prepared to take the plunge. There was no turning back. Perhaps not one in the congregation had the slightest hint of the real depth of the proposal about to be unveiled. Willard Merrill gripped the edges of the pulpit, leaned

28

slightly forward. It was the voice, the manner, of a man inspired.

"We need to bring our country back to God. To the teachings of the Bible. To a new faith, new standards of behavior. Is there one among us who does not seek to change for the better? Then we know what we must do. Jesus set our course for us! He told us! *If any man will come after me, let him deny himself, and take up his cross, and follow me.*

"Are we willing to do this? Or is it too much to ask? Do we say, 'Yes, I'm willing to change, up to a point?' Do we argue, 'Perhaps *he* can follow Jesus but in *my* case I'm not sure I can go all the way?'

"Look at America today. Morally bankrupt. Sexual permissiveness abounds. Lying, cheating a way of life in business and government. Millions addicted to drugs and alcohol. The family no longer a sacred institution. Sin, selfishness, greed prevail—decency, goodness, love are meaningless words.

"And yet our resources are here. The great lessons of Christianity are here. Waiting for us. *God* is waiting for us. To help us. How *long* can we keep *Him* waiting? When will we act? I say to you the time is *now*! Someone, somewhere *must start. We will start, here, now!* We will follow Jesus. Do as He would do!

"Let's take the idea one step further. I have a program. I'm seeking volunteers to participate. I will expect them to take a pledge, a pledge to do nothing whatsoever without first asking the question: 'What would Jesus do?' And once that question is asked, each volunteer will do as Jesus would do in each situation. In his or her job, business, home life, spare-time activities."

He could see odd expressions on their faces. Here and there, a slight smile, or a frown, more in puzzlement than anything else. Mostly, they were staring, awaiting his explanation.

The minister paused to let his message stimulate the deeper emotions of the congregation. His voice was firm, resolute, his manner poised, confident as he continued.

"At the close today, I invite all who are willing to join this program to meet with me downstairs in Activities. We'll discuss

29

our program. The objectives, the problems we're bound to encounter. I'll try to answer questions. And, we'll take this pledge: To act as He would act in every situation regardless of the consequences."

Merrill stared long and hard at his parishioners, then sat down.

Marsha Hoyt sang her own arrangement for the words of Joseph Gilmour.

He leadeth me! O blessed thought!
O words with heavenly comfort fraught!
Whate'er I do, where'er I be,
Still 'tis God's hand that leadeth me.

He leadeth me! He leadeth me!
By His own hand He leadeth me!
His faithful follower I would be,
For by His hand He leadeth me.

People glanced at their neighbors in confusion. Some seemed to be expressing outright astonishment. A few put their heads together and whispered. But Marsha's musical presence kept most of the congregation silent.

In the third pew was Edward Vernon, editor and publisher of the Rockfort Daily News. A longtime member of the church, Ed Vernon served on the building committee. Not a particularly religious man, Vernon, in the early days had attended church to please his wife and daughter. Later, he'd found himself attracted to Willard Merrill's sermons and had volunteered his services.

On Ed Vernon's lined, craggy features now were both pleasure and discomfort. Merrill's idea was appealing. Vernon had been searching for some meaning to the chaos in a troubled world. What could he, personally, do? As a newspaper man, he could see the problems. Could he take a giant step, now, and follow Merrill? Was it practical? Maybe. But if it wasn't, it was worth a try. He smiled to himself in agreement.

Don Turner, Rockfort's biggest car dealer, with three franchises in town, sat quietly near the rear of the church. His wife stared at him, her eyes pleading. Turner was not a regular at the church. His wife was, and now she reached out and took his hand. They moved forward together and knelt in prayer, heads bowed, as the congregation began to file out.

Then something happened to Don Turner. Later he was to describe it as an inner voice. But at that moment all he knew was that nothing would keep him from Merrill's meeting.

Seated behind Vernon was Wes McLain, manager of East-West Lines, a major long-distance trucking firm based in Rockfort. A burly, heavy-set man with jet black hair and piercing dark eyes, McLain was efficient at handling problem drivers and an intricate maze of interstate regulations. He had listened intently as Merrill spoke. He could scarcely believe what he heard. He saw himself back in Georgia and he and his mother were together, reading the Bible. Suddenly the pages of the Great Book came alive in that drab little room and he saw his mother smile softly and nod her approval. Wes McLain knew at that moment he would follow Merrill no matter what the cost.

Moving in the aisles now were Marsha, who had come to join her mother, Grace Hoyt, Virginia Carver, with her brother, Gerald, and their Aunt Geraldine. Rodney Brent, the banker, was with his daughter, Judy.

Facial expressions were more revealing now. There had been time to digest the Reverend's remarks. Most showed outright disbelief. Some were just plain puzzled. A few were thoughtfully silent.

Mrs. Hoyt took Geraldine Carver's arm. "Strangest thing I've ever heard!" she said in a loud whisper. "Are we to join a nunnery? A bit late for that I should think."

"It's just a whim," Geraldine Carver said. "It'll pass. No one can tell me that a good, sensible man like Willard Merrill would really promote such a ridiculous idea. Imagine asking yourself what Jesus would do at our Wednesday bridge game.

You'd be afraid to trump your opponent's ace!"

Mrs. Oswald Yorke, the proclaimer of right and wrong, joined them. "Well, did you ever! I think I'll just go down to Activities and see what this is all about."

"I'll join you," Grace Hoyt said.

They walked up the aisle and Jerry Carver said to his aunt, "Deeny, are you all set to give up your nightly sherry? This town's going to make history. I can see it now in Time magazine. 'Rockfort ready for Second Coming.'"

"That's not funny, Jerry," Virginia Carver said to her brother. "You could attend the meeting and see what he has in mind."

"I'll delegate you to go in my place, Ginny. But don't come home and ask me to wear the collar."

Rodney Brent, the banker, and his daughter Judy paused as they were leaving the church. Brent looked directly at Merrill.

"It's a crazy idea, Reverend. Crazy! You'll never sell it."

9

About thirty parishioners joined Reverend Merrill in Activities. They opened folding chairs and sat at long tables used for functions at which meals were served. The church had a complete kitchen and dishes and utensils to serve two hundred persons.

Willard Merrill began with a brief account of his week-long experience. He admitted frankly his feelings about just getting by, coasting, satisfied. Accepting things that are wrong, without trying to change them. He was careful not to use an accusing attitude. He did not insinuate that any in the small gathering might be guilty of smugness, complacency.

He reminded them of words from Ephesians 2:8-10. *For we are his workmanship, created in Christ Jesus unto good work, which God hath before ordained that we should walk in them.*

"What is this telling us? Doesn't it tell us what our job is here? Isn't it clear, unmistakable? Then why are we not doing as He would have us do? As He has asked us to do? Because we have not listened to Him. We have not taken His words to heart. We're comfortable, content. We give but tokens in our work here in our church. I'm not talking about money— as important as it is— I'm talking about the way we live."

Most listened in thoughtful silence. Ed Vernon, the editor, bent forward, head bowed, as in prayer. Don Turner, the auto dealer, stared transfixed at Merrill. On the rugged features of trucker Wes McLain was a glow of enthusiasm.

Grace Hoyt and Geraldine Carver stared in disbelief.

"How long can 'every one for himself' be our life-style? Think what it would mean if every one among us—if everyone in this great country—were to do as Jesus would do, to live as He would live today. Do you imagine for one moment that we would not see a huge reduction in sin, in human suffering? A great increase in love, kindness—happiness?

"It could happen, my friends. You and I must make it happen. By our sacrifices we will make it happen. I'm not suggesting we abandon all our worldly goods, turn our backs on our achievements and walk the streets in rags. What good would that possibly do? If we ask ourselves at all times 'Am I acting as Jesus would act?' we will continue to prosper. We will *have* our worldly goods. In even greater abundance. Because we will have earned them. *Whatsoever ye shall ask the father in My Name, he will give it to you.* What does in My Name mean? It can only mean one thing. Believe in me. And follow me."

There was total silence before the minister continued. "I want each of you, once you have made up your mind to join with me, to pledge yourself to do everything in your daily life only after asking the question, 'What would Jesus do?' Not just

33

in little things, but in everything. No exceptions. Regardless of the consequences. We will embark on this new road of Christian behavior together. A road I am compelled to take. I dare not begin it alone. I ask your help. I need your help. Those who join me will not find it easy. It will be difficult in our relationships, in our jobs, in our lives at home. But there is no other course."

Marsha Hoyt raised a hand. "How do we know, in a situation, what Jesus would do? How do I decide what His actions would be? This is a different time."

"We must go to the source," Merrill said. "We must study Jesus. We must follow the words of I John in 3:18. *Let us not love in word, neither in tongue; but in deed and in truth.*

"We all react differently," Ed Vernon said. "Your idea of what Jesus would do in a given situation might not be the same as mine."

"We must take that as it comes. If each of us is dedicated to a single purpose—to make this idea work for us right here and now—we will find the way. We have only to ask and it shall be revealed to us."

Wes McLain said: "What will people say? Won't they say, 'Oh, Jesus would never do that'?"

"Perhaps. But we must follow our standards for Christian action regardless."

"We can do it," Don Turner said quietly. "I know we can."

"Reverend," Mrs. Oswald Yorke said haughtily, "I disagree with you. I'm sorry but I do. We're in the last years of the twentieth century, not back in Year One riding around on camels."

"Of course not," Virginia Carver broke in. "But what the Reverend says makes sense to me. I don't think one of us can deny what he says. We can't say, 'everything's just wonderful.' Things *aren't* wonderful! And, 'I'm such a good person. I do so much for others.' I..."

34

"That's absurd," Mrs. Yorke said. "No one in this church does more—in proportion to the time and money available—than I. Have you ever heard of Internal Revenue?"

"It's not a question of money," Merrill said. "I thought I'd covered that. All we must do is to be honest with ourselves. We must truly follow Jesus' teachings. Not in a fanatical way. Not half-heartedly either. We must remember this: Jesus set an example for the world to follow. Up to now, the world has not followed. Far from it. We must follow. We must..."

Geraldine Carver broke in. "We are to do this? The *world* ignores Jesus' teachings! But *we* must follow? This small group, out of the blue, must suddenly take the lead, and then the world, country by country, will follow? What's so special about Rockfort? About us? Why Rockfort? Why us?"

"I can see why you'd ask that," Merrill said calmly. "It isn't our job to change the world. Our job is to change ourselves. As we change, others will change. You'll see that happen. Once we ask Jesus to tell us what He would do in each situation, we'll do it. Then others will do it."

Ellen Heath, wife of Roger Heath, the professor of political science at nearby Lincoln College, spoke up. "Time is running out. With the world the way it is, something must be done. And Jesus told us what to do."

There were more questions and comments. Then the minister asked those who were ready to make the commitment to report their experiences to the group each week at a meeting, at the same time on Sundays.

"I now ask those in agreement to join me in prayer."

As if that were a signal, Mrs. Yorke, Grace Hoyt, Geraldine Carver and eight others left the hall. Merrill waited until the last one had disappeared up the stairway. "We'll all kneel and pray silently—pray that the Holy Spirit will lead us at this important time."

A strange silence descended on the room, a Presence that was not there before.

Later, all were to recall a feeling of Divine power, a sense of peace and tranquility, a general well-being never before experienced.

To Wes McLain it was startling. "It was as though I was weightless," he explained. "I had absolutely no burden of any sort, no worry, no fear, no anxiety. I was completely at ease."

In all, eighteen made the commitment. They included Marsha, Virginia, Ed Vernon, Don and Sara Turner, Wes McLain and Ellen Heath.

They remained for another hour, talking excitedly over their new life-to-be. When they had gone, Willard Merrill fell to his knees and prayed again. He asked for guidance, for strength, for wisdom. Most of all, he prayed that his program would not bring unbearable stress and problems to the wonderful people who were now with him in his search for the Right Way, for the course that Jesus had taught.

It was a sobering moment. And it was disturbing. He knew Rockfort would protest. Rockfort would scorn, ridicule, criticize. There would be no ready acceptance, no rush to join Merrill's followers of Jesus—"that crazy little band of crackpots." Human nature always resisted. The mass mind, blind in its adherence to selfishness, pettiness, anxiety, greed and dishonesty, would do its best to quickly wipe out Merrill's new program before it could get underway.

Willard Merrill raised his eyes to Heaven.

Dear Jesus, help me, give me strength to do Thy work. Show me the way!

10

"I was shocked," Ann Merrill said later on Sunday afternoon—a Sunday that was to be remembered in Rockfort as The Day It All Started.

"The looks on their faces! They just sat there and stared at you as if you'd lost your mind. Maybe you have. I hope it's only temporary, like two-day flu. All sorts of people came up to me. I didn't know what to say. I just tried to smile."

"I half expected you might join us downstairs."

"Will, I told you yesterday how I felt. Something's got into you that's making you do this very strange thing. I don't know what it is. I pray you'll come to your senses before it's too late. It's one thing to be a minister. It's quite another to start playing God."

"It's not that at all."

"Then what do you call it?"

"Living as Jesus would have us live. Doing as He would do. It must start sometime, somewhere."

"Why did it need to start at the corner of Beech Lane and Brook Road, in Rockfort, on the first Sunday in June?"

Willard Merrill spoke softly. "Darling, your reaction is quite normal. I understand. All I ask is—give this idea a chance. Don't shoot it down before it takes off."

"I won't do any shooting. But the confused souls of the Pleasant Valley Church who once loved you are probably loading up right now."

11

In the seventh inning, the St. Louis Cardinals and the Philadelphia Phillies were tied, 3 to 3, when Ed Vernon surprised his wife, Barbara, and his teen daughter, Hildy, by switching off the set.

"Dad! Turning off the Cards? Your team!"

"I've been thinking about Will Merrill's idea."

"Are you going to do an editorial on it?" Barbara asked.

He shrugged. "I hadn't thought of that yet."

37

"I've never heard Reverend Merrill so sincere."

"What does it mean, Dad? How do you follow Jesus? Follow him where?"

"I'm not really sure. But we have to start somewhere." He put his arms around them. "I made the pledge. I promised we'd go along, all the way."

"Are you including us?"

"Yes, honey. We're in this together. I just hope you'll be able to cooperate if the going gets rough."

"Why should it?" Hildy asked.

Ed Vernon smiled. "The life of Jesus was not an easy one."

"But this is today, not Biblical times," Barbara said.

"Most of today's problems are similar. Worse. The morals and ethics of society..." He shook his head sadly. "The world's in a sad state. What's the answer? The teachings of Jesus! I don't know any other. At least, it's worth a try."

Ed Vernon walked over to a window and looked out, thoughtfully, on Long Pond. He loved his home. It was a comfortable three-bedroom Colonial on three-quarters of an acre. There was a dock and the Vernon's trim, twenty-four foot cruiser had been in the water since mid-April. Boating, fishing, the closeness of the Vernons, Hildy's many high-school activities, Barbara's volunteer social work. Life was good.

Yet, in spite of the good life, Ed Vernon worried. He worried about the world and the way things were going. Barbara and he might get through life all right, but what about Hildy... the future? Should he just stand by and worry? Or as a crusading editor, an idealist, do something about it?

Barbara had left the room to prepare dinner. Hildy went upstairs to wash her hair. Ed Vernon stood silently, gazing out the window. Would he really have the strength to make the tough decisions that were inevitable? This wasn't just another new promise, like a New Year's resolution. He knew Will Merrill too well not to anticipate the seriousness of the minister's decision.

He had taken the pledge. Voluntarily. Those who had chosen not to go along had left the meeting. He, Ed Vernon, had stayed. Signed up.

But on his way home from church, he had struggled with the huge problems that would surely arise in trying to live up to the pledge. Alone now in the comfortable living room, late on Sunday afternoon, the problems, still only vaguely defined, loomed larger than ever. Would he be willing to face them? Assume for the moment that his family would cooperate. What about his business? What about the *Daily News,* a power in Rockfort for 87 years?

There was no way for Ed Vernon to do as Jesus would do in his personal and home life and continue business as usual at the *News.* Will Merrill had made it clear. "In every situation today and every day we will ask ourselves: What would Jesus do? We will change our thinking, our actions, reactions. We will change our entire way of life to follow Him. Do as He would do."

Ed Vernon could see his troubles gathering like dark clouds before a summer storm. But he had made his commitment. He would not turn back. He would not send word to Merrill: "Sorry, Will, but I've thought it over carefully and I've decided to withdraw. Your plan is wonderful, but in my case..."

No. Absolutely no! He would stick. He would become a tower of strength in the program. He would see every problem as an opportunity. If only...

He sank to his knees and prayed. He prayed to the one Power that Will Merrill always explained so clearly. He thought of a line he had written years ago on the back of a church program after a Merrill sermon: *As we have therefore opportunity, let us do good unto all men.* It was from Galatians 6:10. He had never forgotten it. Yes, this was *his* opportunity. The opportunity he had been seeking!

He recalled another selection, from Hebrews 13:5. *I will never leave thee, nor forsake thee.*

As he prayed, he concentrated his thoughts on these two Bible excerpts. The opportunity is there. I will take advantage of it. I'm in the group. I've given my word. I'll not forsake them.

He remained kneeling for a long time. The empty feeling of anxiety left him. Gradually, he felt a return of energy. A quiet composure seemed to come from somewhere above and envelope his mind and body. Suddenly he felt exhilarated, then confident.

12

Don Turner hadn't attended church in almost two months until the Sunday of Reverend Merrill's astounding proposal. His Sunday mornings customarily were devoted to a review of his week's business. Success had not come easily to Don Turner. The car business was notoriously a dog-eat-dog activity. Sell, sell, sell. Deal, deal, deal. Don't let a prospect walk out the door. He might go to a competitor.

Operation of three car dealerships had made Turner the highest volume dealer in the city and placed him among the top ten in the state. The business was computerized. Every car, every part in inventory was immediately identifiable. At the end of each week, sales, service revenue, payroll, accounts payable—even exact cash balances—were detailed on a printout. Don had installed a computer terminal at home in his den. Sunday mornings would find him sitting at the keyboard, punching out statistics.

Success, for Don Turner, meant possessions, expensive ones. A winter home on St. Croix. A 38-foot Beneteau ocean-going yacht. Their daughter, Lynn, at exclusive Millbrook School. The Turners were always striving for something more. They entertained lavishly. If you came to a party at the Turners you couldn't escape the display of prosperity. Photos of the boat, the island home. You knew the Turners had everything.

You didn't know they were short on happiness. Sara Turner was in her second year of analysis with one of Rockfort's most expensive psychiatrists. Lynn Turner, home on vacation, had brought along four pairs of jeans that hadn't been washed in months and a bagful of cassettes featuring rock bands. And a headful of liberal, anti-social ideas. Big business was rotten. Politicians were crooks. Religion a rip-off.

Lynn slept till noon, spent her evenings at discos and fought with her mother over sloppy clothes, an untidy room and junk foods.

For a long time Sara Turner knew something was missing. Gradually she began to impress this on Don. She talked often of a smaller home, a simpler life. Don thought of a tent pitched by a stream somewhere in Colorado, a new set of values, friends who were not always trying to impress others. They had been on the dollar merry-go-round for a long time. But how to get off?

Don and Sara had been in that mood on this Sunday.

The Turners were invited to the Mason's buffet brunch in West Rockfort, near the church. "I might as well go along with you," Don had said to Sara. "Then after church we'll join the crowd at Pete and Jean's."

They never made it to the brunch.

During Will Merrill's sermon, Sara Turner stared silently at her husband, her eyes saying, "Can't we at least try?" After the service, the Turners had remained kneeling for a long time. They had stayed for the group meeting and taken the pledge. Afterwards, with few words passing between them, they went to the Old Mill for lunch.

"I want to do it," Don said over coffee.

"Do you have any idea what it'll mean?"

"Not really. But something tells me we have to do it."

"Don, you're in a tough business. Can you sell cars in the same way if you try to live as Jesus would live? Won't it be difficult?"

"Probably." He grasped her hand. "But we can do it—together."

Sara Turner smiled. "That's one of the nicest things you've ever said to me."

They walked out of the restaurant in a glow of excitement.

That evening, before retiring, for the first time Don and Sara Turner knelt together in prayer.

13

Wes McLain left Will Merrill's meeting with enthusiasm.

Raised in a small town in rural Georgia, Wes was taught to appreciate the Bible early in life. His mother taught him to read it every night. Before he was through high school, to help support his widowed mother, Wes got a job driving a produce truck from Macon to Augusta.

Bigger rigs and longer routes followed. Living a rough life on interstate highways, sleeping in second-rate motels and eating in shabby diners, Wes McLain held to his love of the Bible. He read it every night before retiring. After his marriage, he tried unsuccessfully to persuade his wife, Alice, to join him at church and in Bible readings. She preferred to bury herself in *Cosmopolitan* and romance novels. Their son, Jeff, sided with his mother, and Wes McLain went to church alone on Sundays.

He worked his way up through various jobs and for ten years had been general manager of East-West Lines, a large trucking firm in Rockfort. The McLain's owned a modest ranch home in a new development adjoining West Rockfort. Wes looked forward to his Sundays. He made a habit of noting particular Bible passages used by Will Merrill. When he got home he would read over the section again and again in his basement workshop where he knew he would be uninterrupted. Jeff hated anything resembling tools or carpentry.

On this Sunday, Wes McLain was in a state of pure enchantment. He had searched for so long. What can I do, Lord, to be closer? How can I do more to make others see the way? Countless times he had asked himself these questions—in difficult situations at work, in trying to understand Alice's love of possessions and her escapist time-wasting habits, in living with Jeff's indifference to the things that make life worthwhile.

Here, finally, was the answer. Surely Alice and Jeff would see what he had struggled to give them over the years. The Word was there, so clear, so easy to grasp. The answer to everything was in following Jesus. In doing as He would do. It was so simple. It was what his mother, without realizing it, had instilled in him.

They were in the kitchen when he came in, Alice busy with Sunday dinner, Jeff holding a can of soda. Wes sat on a stool at the snack counter. For a few moments he simply beamed at them expectantly. Will Merrill was divinely inspired. There was no other explanation. At last, Wes McLain would experience the bonds of a common faith with his family.

He heard himself talking as if a stranger were speaking. His voice seemed to come from a far part of the kitchen, fusing with sounds of cabinet doors closing, dishes rattling, ice cubes dropping into a tall glass, the snap of a soda-can opener.

"...Reverend Merrill was unbelievable...his new ideas... we have a group formed to meet every week...the plan...do as Jesus would do...in everything...Merrill explained it so well...we talk these things...we go to church...but we don't *do* them...I can see a whole new life...here's what it comes down to..."

Jeff actually pulled a chair away from the kitchen table and quietly sat down. Alice kept at her task but her moves were slower. Her face was immobile. She appeared to be hanging on every word. She removed a casserole from the oven and stood holding it for a few seconds before placing it on a heat-proof pad. When she turned to look at Wes, amazement had traced fine lines in her cheeks and above her eyes.

"...What we have to do is think...every time before we act or speak...are we following Jesus?...do you know how many we have in the group?...Ed Vernon came in...so did Don Turner...best thing ever happened in this city...I want you two to come to the next meeting...see what I mean...all our old ideas have to go...this is for real...it'll change our lives... I'm starting in the morning down at the terminal...we can't go on like before..."

When he had finished there was silence.

"Are you all right, Pop?"

"I want you both to pray with me."

"Supper's ready," Alice announced.

"Boy, that preacher man really got to you!"

Wes' great moment was shattered. For a time he had foolishly believed they would change, go along with him. Then the old truism crept into his consciousness: You can't change a person unless he wants to change.

He protested for a while but they were too much for him. There was no use going on. Wes McLain rose from his seat and fled down the cellar stairs to his workshop and his Bible.

On his knees, he prayed for help, for guidance, for strength. He didn't hear the strident call.

"Your supper's getting cold!"

His eyes were glued to Isaiah 43:2. *When thou passest through the waters, I will be with thee; and through the rivers, they shall not overflow thee: when thou walkest through the fire, thou shalt not be burned; neither shall the flame kindle upon thee.*

Wes McLain knew he was right. He would go forward. No matter what obstacles might appear. He would go all the way.

44

14

"Are you ready for dinner?" Judy Brent asked indifferently. Her father didn't look up from his copy of Barron's. "Any time," he mumbled.

"Do you resent my being here? I can't help it if my marriage broke up."

"Of course not! I love you, you know that. And I'm happy to have you home again. It was lonesome here after your mother died. But I sometimes wish you'd find something to do. Without the country club and that pool you'd be lost."

They sat at the long mahogany dinner table.

"By the time we've finished, *60 Minutes* will be on."

"It's a bore," Judy grumbled.

"Find something else."

They ate in silence for a few minutes.

"What was that stuff in church all about?" Judy finally asked.

"Nonsense. Pure claptrap. I never thought I'd hear Merrill talk such silliness."

"You don't think they can do it?"

"Do what?"

"Live as Jesus would live. Isn't that what he wants to promote?"

"Of course they can't. Naturally, there'll always be a few who'll try. Any new crackpot idea will always find a few suckers. Judy, there are at least a thousand religious cults in this country right now. We don't need another one. We certainly don't need one popping up in our church."

"Who can stop it?"

"If Merrill wants to make a fool of himself, that's up to him. But most of the regulars won't follow him. They won't say much but they won't chant hymns at the corner of Broad and Main either. Merrill will find he has to go it pretty much alone. He'll find such absurd behavior won't help the cash flow. People won't give as much. I'll certainly review my pledge."

"I knew you'd judge it in terms of money."

"What else is there?"

15

Sunday afternoon Jerry Carver came home from tennis at the Rockfort Country Club. He showered, got into designer bright yellow jeans and an offwhite terry shirt, and made himself a gin and tonic.

He joined his sister and his aunt on the screened porch on the west end of the huge house. "Two guys at the club asked me about Merrill's pitch this morning. Word gets around fast. What's the old boy trying to do, Ginny?"

"If you'd come to the meeting you'd know. A number of us joined the program."

Jerry laughed. "So it's a program, huh? A Jesus program! Everybody stops sinning!"

"It's more than that."

Geraldine Carver, who was 64 and as sharp as a person half that age, said: "I don't smoke. I'm a little old for romance. But I love a glass of sherry. So what am I supposed to stop doing?"

"Darling, you don't do bad things and you don't think bad thoughts," Virginia said easily. "We want you to go right on, having fun, enjoying life. You've earned it. If I start acting a little strange in this thing, I know you'll forgive me."

Her aunt smiled. "I'd forgive you if you picked out a nice man and got married. But I suppose that's asking too much. Jerry's just as bad. Half the girls in this town have their eyes on him but he won't get himself roped. Takes after his father."

"I'm enjoying life too much to get married," Jerry said.

Virginia looked at him fondly. She loved him, but worried about his wasted life.

46

"What's this program all about?" Jerry asked.

Virginia explained Reverend Merrill's idea. There was a silence. Then Geraldine Carver said, "I may have been too harsh on Will Merrill this morning. We certainly can use more Godliness in the world. This country ought to set a better example and we don't. But if Merrill thinks he can get people going around acting like Jesus Christ, he's out of his mind. I can see that you're in it whole hog, Ginny. A mistake. It'll only cost you money."

Geraldine picked up her empty sherry glass and went into the house.

"I'm afraid this is one time I don't agree with Deeny," said Virginia.

"Oh, come on, Gin. You don't really buy this Jesus nonsense, do you? Do as Jesus would do? What would He do, today?"

Quietly, seriously, Virginia replied. "He tells us. In the Bible. He tells us what we have to do—to lead a good life, to help others."

Jerry sipped his drink. "To hell with others. Take care of yourself. Enjoy yourself. That's my philosophy."

"Don't you think there's more to life, Jerry, than just ourselves? Such as love of others. Faith. Belief...?"

"No. I'm afraid I don't. I'm not what you'd call a man of faith."

Virginia rose, kissed her brother in the forehead and smiled sadly. "You're incorrigible."

Seriously, with resolute steps, she went to her suite of rooms. She kneeled, opened her Bible to Mark 11:24. *Therefore I tell you, whatever you ask for in prayer, believe that you will receive it, and it will be yours.*

Virginia Carver prayed, prayed hard. She prayed for help—to succeed in her new life. And she prayed for her brother.

47

16

With her father at the Country Club Sunday afternoon, Marsha Hoyt hoped to avoid any further discussions with her mother about Reverend Merrill's program. But Mrs. Hoyt took the initiative and approached Marsha in the sun room.

"Marsha, I have something to say to you. You're a beautiful girl. You're very talented. Do I have to remind you that you were the beauty queen at the university? The star of every show? That I sacrificed so you could study voice and acting, to have a career? And what happened with that career? Nothing. You sing in church! How long do you plan to go on? 'Till you're forty?"

Marsha said nothing.

"It wasn't so bad when you were just out of school. But now—this Jesus thing! You simply can't allow yourself to be taken in by that man's incredible ideas. Following Jesus in every thought and act! How in God's name would one do that? It's ridiculous! Is Jesus going to pay our taxes? The mortgage? Well let me tell you this—if you start giving more of your time to the church, and to this impossible idea of his, you'll do it without any support from me."

Mrs. Hoyt swept out, leaving Marsha shaken.

July

1

Ed Vernon spread the Monday morning *News* on his desk. He had slept fitfully, wrestling with both enthusiasm for his new life and a persistent anxiety he could not shake. The headlines in his paper were shocking; he saw them this morning in a new light.

Teen Drug Use Mounts. Soviets Test New A-Weapon. Local Divorce Rate Up. Unmarried Mother, 17, dies in Fire. Judge Indicted on Bribery Charge. Three Children Sexually Abused.

On and on it went. So much sin! So much suffering! Will Merrill was right. The world was in need of help, an inspired leadership.

Vernon took a pad and made notes as he went through each page. He checked news stories, features, advertisements. Then he called in Dana Bell, managing editor and his right-hand man. Bell was a slender man, 55, slightly stooped and with receding gray-brown hair. He was a good newspaper man, a pro; the 18 reporters liked his open manner and respected his ability.

Vernon waved Bell to a seat and told him what had happened at the church; he explained the program. Bell's amiable expression slowly changed to one of confusion, then disbelief as Vernon talked.

"We're going to make some changes, Dana. Not all at once—over a period of a few weeks. I want you to try to understand my reasons.

"As soon as our contracts expire, we'll drop all advertising for racing, bars and liquor stores, 'R' rated films..."

"That lineage runs into big money!"

"We're not simply giving lip service to this program, Dana. Every step of the way we're going to ask ourselves: 'What would Jesus do?' and then act accordingly. Drinking, sexual permissiveness, gambling—anything that's contrary to the teaching of Jesus—will no longer be publicized in the paper."

"Ed, I don't believe I'm hearing this from you." Bell rose and paced nervously in front of Vernon's desk. "Are you also saying that our news coverage of racing will be cut back?"

"Eliminated. Racing in itself may be all right but people become addicted. They can't stop betting. Their families suffer."

"But, Ed. We can't do it! Thousands of sports fans depend on us. They don't buy the *Herald* because it's too junky. They depend on us, for complete coverage."

Ed Vernon shoved the morning *News* across the desk.

"Your department will change in other ways, too. Violence, crime, dishonesty—all these things will no longer be featured by the *News*."

"What! If there's a stabbing down in Sin City we ignore it? You can't run a paper that way!"

"Dana. Let's cover things that are good. Christian family life, churches and schools that are doing good. People who are doing good, helping others. There's plenty of news out there without glamorizing evil. We don't need to concentrate on everything that's wrong. Let's expand our coverage of other sports and business, add more home and garden features, self-help material, book reviews."

Dana Bell shook his head in disbelief. They argued for an hour. Ed Vernon held to his position. It was the same, later in the morning, with the paper's advertising manager. When he was told the ban extended to ads for massage parlors and escort services, he was speechless.

By mid-afternoon, word had spread like a brush fire. One after another the *News* department heads trooped into the executive offices to hear for themselves what they found impossible to believe. Then came the advertising salesmen, followed by the typesetters, pressmen and route men.

Each saw the new restrictions as a dreadful mistake. When one ad salesman estimated how much money his department would lose, a dozen fellow workers at once saw the paper failing. When the sports editor reminded his colleagues that daily racing news always ranked high in readership, it was predicted that circulation would fall drastically.

Eventually, all went back to work, grumbling. The first edition of the *News* hit the street each night at 11. From four on in the afternoon, everyone was too busy to think about Incredible Monday. Later, as they left work in two's and three's, they exchanged gripes and direful predictions. The whole idea was silly, stupid. Vernon would back down. He had to.

Weary and more worried than at any time in his life, Ed Vernon sat at his desk in the quiet of late evening. The day had been totally exhausting. At nine, he phoned Barbara to say he'd be late. The reactions had been more vehement than he'd foreseen. Was he on the right course? Could he really do this thing and survive? Nearly three hundred people thought he was wrong, thought he was, quite frankly, a crackpot, a man bent on destroying the *News* and the jobs it supported.

He reached for the phone and dialed Willard Merrill.

"It's bad over here."

"I'm sure it is. Hold steady, Ed. Don't get discouraged. Pray. Pray right now before you leave your office. I'll pray here, too. We're prayer Christians. Believers. Believers in Jesus Christ. That is our only course. Pray for guidance, for right action and for God's help."

Ed Vernon put down the phone and slowly rose from his desk. He closed the door and kneeled in prayer. I know I am right in what I'm doing. No one said it would be easy. It is the way to go, the only way. Oh, Lord, give me the strength to carry on. Show me the way. Let Divine intelligence dwell in every person on this newspaper, give us the strength to move forward, to follow Jesus, to do as He would do. Tonight and every day. Amen.

When he walked to the elevator, Vernon met Dana Bell leaving the newsroom. They went to the ground floor without speaking. At the front door, the managing editor paused.

"This'll never work, Ed."

2

By late Monday, Don Turner had ordered an end to add-ons. An add-on, or "market adjustment," was a sum added to the list price of a car when a model was in short supply.

Don also ordered a change in trade-in policy. From now on, a prospective buyer was to be given a fair market price for his old car regardless of how much he paid for his new car or how many expensive options he ordered. And deceptive "bait and switch" advertising was to end. No longer would full-page Turner ads feature low come-on prices of stripped economy models—sometimes not even available—to lure customers into the showroom and trade them up to much higher priced cars.

"The competition up and down Northern Boulevard will laugh at us!" cried Jed Benson, the sales manager. "It'll cut our margins. The men will earn less. Showroom traffic will fall off. Look, so you're into a new gimmick at your church. So, okay. That's your business. But don't louse up our operation here!"

Don Turner knew his staff. And he knew the automobile business. He'd never be able to change the thinking of Benson, a valuable man. The salesmen would be even tougher. To them, the dollar was everything. Sales had been good. Any restriction on earnings from a religious crusader would send the better salesmen scurrying down the Boulevard to other dealers.

In service it would be the same story. With lower charges favoring the customer, the mechanics would earn less.

At six o'clock Benson came into Turner's office. "I'll be back after dinner. Think it over carefully, Don. You'll see this whole idea's crazy. We've had three good months in a row. We're going good. I know you're trying to do a fine thing. But keep it under wraps. Around the house and all that stuff. Not here, Don. Not here."

The strain of the long day showed in Turner's face. His chin sagged. There was puffiness under his eyes. He was very tired and he looked it. He dialed the house and Sara answered at once.

"I've been worried about you. How did it go?"

"No good," he said despairingly. "Jed is violently opposed. They'll all be as soon as word gets around. He thinks I'll mull things over tonight and change my mind. He's sure of it."

"Then he doesn't know you very well."

"I can see their side. Business will really suffer."

"But you have to stand your ground. You took a pledge and I'm part of it! How long will you be there?"

"Couple of hours. Our sale is still on."

"Pray. Pray, Don. And I will, too."

Within 30 minutes the door to Turner's office opened and Willard Merrill walked in. He sat in a huge leather-covered chair facing the desk.

"Sara called. I decided to come over."

Turner told the minister of the day's happenings.

"I don't know—." His voice trailed off as though it was too much effort to go on.

Willard Merrill took a small Bible from his pocket. He read from Matthew 11:28. *Come unto me, all ye that labour and are heavy laden, and I will give you rest.* As he continued with the verse, Turner began to relax. The tenseness eased in his face muscles and he sat up in his chair and leaned forward across the desk. After a long pause, he spoke softly.

"Do you really think we can do this thing, Will?"

"I'm positive of it."

"I knew it wouldn't be easy, but—"

"Let's try to work it out together. We know that God is everywhere present in our experience. The Holy Spirit is always at work, guiding us in everything we do. Our source is God. In following Jesus, the action of God is working in us, with us, through us. We must look beyond our immediate trials, our obstacles, to the one purpose, the one central idea in our new lives—which is to ask ourselves, 'What would Jesus do?' Let's join together now and truly visualize what Jesus would do right here in your office, in Rockfort, on Monday evening at seven o'clock. Knowing our course to be right, would He not say, from Hebrews 11:1, *Now faith is the substance of things hoped for, the evidence of things not seen?*

"Certainly He would. We are sure of what we are doing, Don. We have faith that it is right. We are certain of the result. If the path is clear and right, and our faith is complete, then we will succeed. We will triumph. Now, let's kneel together and lift our thoughts in truth, in the assurance that our only right course is to follow Jesus, right here and now."

They prayed together. Finally, they rose. Don Turner turned out his office lights and waved to the showroom crew. He walked with Merrill to the minister's car.

"Thank you for coming over, Will. I can face tomorrow now. Without being afraid."

3

From his office on the third floor of East-West Lines, Wes McLain could survey 36 loading bays where up to 250 long-haul trailers in a single week were loaded or unloaded with merchandise.

For a week now, the newest wave of stealing had operated openly, blatantly, almost within his view. It was as if East-West checkers and the long-haul drivers either considered McLain to be uninterested in their crimes or assumed he was powerless to stop them.

He called in his superintendent, big Jim Akers, a rugged man who had worked his way up from loading, checking, dispatching.

"Jim, we're back where we were last winter. I thought we'd licked the skimoff with the new locking system." Wes shuffled a batch of green and white forms on his desk. "Insurance claims. Stuff's disappearing like snow in July. Last month alone we lost twenty-five TV's, eighteen VCR's and eight micro ovens."

Akers shrugged. "We spot check but it don't help. When they drop a shipment in Des Moines or Pittsburg, they drop a couple units for theirselves."

"What are we doing about it?"

"We see bills is short, we report 'em. The shipper gets tagged by the receiver because he don't get what he ordered. It goes to insurance. Takes weeks. That's about it. You can't prove nothin' unless you hit 'em walkin' away with it."

"What about the shop boss?"

"Rollie? You kiddin'? Rollie's the union rep. He won't rock any boats."

"It's time he did."

Akers shook his head. "You mess with Rollie you get a slowdown, a sickout, maybe even a work stoppage."

Alone at his desk, McLain knew he could wait no longer. He had to act. If a showdown meant trouble with the union, then Wes McLain would face the problem squarely. Wes knew any kind of work interruption, if it came from pressure by him, would bring immediate reaction from the main office in Chicago. "Your job is strictly profit-supported, McLain," they had told him often. "Don't louse up. Keep things moving. Understand?"

McLain was exhausted when he left the office. The East-West fiscal-year audit was in progress. This meant a team of accountants had been at his elbow throughout the day. There had been numerous long-distance calls. And now the scam was back, the skimoff that he could no longer ignore. He was half-way home when he pulled over, stopped his car. He knew he could not talk about his problems with Alice and Jeff. They would immediately link his troubles to the new program at the church. He could hear them now.

"Why don't you phone Jesus, Dad?"

"Nobody's a saint, Wes. You can't reform the world, or even one driver."

"Can't you bring these bad guys to church with you?"

He turned around and drove to Willard Merrill's house.

"Come in, Wes."

Merrill led the way to his study.

Wes McLain described the situation at East-West. He admitted that at another time he might not have taken action. But he had to now. After yesterday's meeting, after taking the pledge. His face was lined, grim. He sat in front of the minister's desk, clenching his hands, speaking in a low, grating voice.

"Can I do it, Reverend? Can I really live as Jesus would live? Do as He would do? This is a rough business. Drivers are a tough bunch, you know that. Many are good, honest. But others—"

"Wes," Merrill spoke firmly. "We can only go forward. Whatever it takes. Whatever the sacrifices. We're a small group. Dedicated. We'll grow. Others will come in. Those of us who are pioneers will have it very rough for a while. But we will win. We will triumph!"

"My family won't help. And I can't afford to risk my job. Can I really go it alone?"

Merrill smiled faintly. "It may surprise you to know that Ann thinks *I'm* out of my mind."

"That's hard to believe."

"We'll have more than just ridicule, Wes. We'll have real opposition. People oppose anything they don't know or understand. And, unfortunately, they don't know or understand very much about Jesus, or his teachings. That's why they won't accept it—at first."

"My mother would have accepted it," McLain said wistfully. "She taught me the Bible. Do you know what her favorite quotation was? It was from John 14:27. I think I learned to say it at about the age of seven. *Let not your heart be troubled, neither let it be afraid."*

Willard Merrill gestured, indicating that they kneel in prayer. He said, "And later on in John, our entire reason for being is clear: *Follow me."*

Wes McLain arrived home after Alice and Jeff had finished dinner. They were somewhere upstairs. He made himself a sandwich and went down to his workshop, preferring to avoid television, the phone, all conversation.

He recalled what Reverend Merrill had said. Ridicule would continue; he'd seen it in his own home. Sacrifices would be needed. What of it? His mother had sacrificed for her children. She had done her very best. Wasn't that the answer right now? Sacrifice. And do your best to live up to the pledge. Don't let them throw you off course.

By the time he came upstairs his wife and son were securely rooted in front of the television set. Exhausted, he continued on up to bed. He opened his Bible and found a passage— Matthew 11:28-30—he had loved so many years ago back in Georgia. *Come to me, all you who are weary and burdened, and I will give you rest. Take my yoke upon you and learn from me, for I am gentle and humble in heart, and you will find rest for your souls.*

4

Marsha enjoyed lunching with Virginia on the terrace at Brooklawn, the Carver estate overlooking a rolling green lawn and sparkling pool. The setting was beautiful, the food sumptuous.

Today, Monday, was no exception. And they had been joined by Jerry. When he heard Marsha was coming to lunch, he had cancelled his usual date at the Rockfort City Club.

"Have you girls decided on your project?"

"No," answered Virginia. "We planned to talk to Willard last week but he was pretty busy. We expect to see him in a day or so."

"Well, I'll let you two save the world." He rose from the table.

Marsha smiled understandingly. "If we can just save one person we'll be happy."

"Or just help one person," replied Virginia.

"There are a lot of them need saving down in Sin City," said Jerry, referring to the slum area of Rockfort. He walked across the terrace to the house.

"Have a date at the club. See you in church!"

Marsha and Virginia left the table and walked slowly around the pool area. Marsha was wearing white slacks and a bright green, short-sleeved shirt. Her long auburn hair was held by a white head band. "So many need help," she said. "The homeless, those on drugs, alcohol. Those out of work a long time."

"We'll come up with a plan," Ginny said. "Something Jesus would do, if he were alive today."

"Something that *needs* to be done," Marsha said.

Ginny said, "Let's both think it through, separately, agree on the idea, and then discuss it with Willard."

"We'll meet Wednesday at my place as a starter. Then we'll call Willard."

Marsha was on the flagstone walkway, headed for her car, when Jerry, in a bright red sports jacket, came out of the house and hurried to join her.

"Everything settled?"

"Until our next meeting."

They paused in the wide blacktop parking area. Jerry grasped the door handle of Marsha's Skylark. He was in no hurry to open the door.

"Whoever it is you're about to help will be pretty lucky. Why can't I be poor?"

She said easily, "Poor doesn't suit your style."

"There's a new French restaurant on Five Mile Road. How about dinner tonight?"

Marsha looked away. Then she said: "Thanks, but I can't."

"Tomorrow night?"

"I'm sorry, Jerry."

She smiled at him and he held the car door for her. Thoughtfully Jerry watched her car disappear down the driveway. Then he climbed into his 300ZX and headed for the City Club.

The Rockfort City Club was a leftover from the '20's when a group of the city's richest men, seeking privacy, pooled a million dollars to build their own private club.

A four-story brick building near the center of town, the club was more elaborate than one would expect in a medium-size city. It included a large second-floor dining room, several small rooms for private affairs, card and billiard rooms and a basement pool. On the upper floors were sleeping rooms for out-of-town guests.

The deep mahogany walls and shining marble floors bespoke exclusivity and wealth. Rockfort's richest, most successful men

—manufacturers, merchants, bankers and lawyers—met, ate, drank and did business here. This was the Establishment.

And the Establishment ran Rockfort.

Jerry walked into the lobby as stragglers from the late luncheon crowd were leaving. Among them were two attorneys from Rockfort's leading law firm.

"Hey, Jerry," Charley Gilmore said. "What's going on at that church of yours?"

"Nothing, really."

"My wife says half the congregation's on some kind of Jesus kick."

"Is Reverend Merrill going on television? Like Bob Schuller and Jimmy Swaggart?" asked Bart Flynn.

Jerry hurried past them into the bar where he was routinely served scotch on the rocks. He walked quickly into the adjourning card room.

"You're late!" Andy Harkness, Jerry's closest friend, was at a table shuffling cards. Andy had inherited many millions from his father who had owned a chain of drug stores in the mid-West. Like Jerry, he did not work.

"I had lunch at home," explained Jerry, sitting down.

"Oh, Marsha must have been there. The only time you miss lunch here is when she's lunching at your place."

Jerry was pensive. Andy dealt the cards.

"How you making out there, with Marsha?"

"I'm not. I keep trying, but she won't have anything to do with me!"

5

As Marsha approached the porch of her home, the door opened suddenly. Her mother stood beaming.

"Marsha, darling. We have a guest!"

Mrs. Hoyt grabbed her daughter's arm and whispered. "Oh, Marsha. It's so exciting. So wonderful!"

60

They entered the living room, Marsha curious and puzzled. Eldon Hoyt and the guest rose. He was an over-weight middle-aged man with a round body and a round face, the latter dominated by large black horn-rimmed glasses.

"This is Mr. Goodman, from New York, dear," announced Mrs. Hoyt.

Ace Goodman shook Marsha's hand vigorously and talked fast as they sat down.

"I'm head of talent, Miss Hoyt, at General Television. We're planning a new television musical series next season featuring new talent. We've been following you for a long time. I saw you at the university in *The King and I* and *Kiss Me Kate*. You have a fine voice. You're very beautiful. We believe you have a career—"

"Oh, isn't that wonderful! A star—" exclaimed Mrs. Hoyt.

"We're prepared to start you at a thousand dollars a week, fifty-two thousand a year, with options—"

"Fifty-two thousand a year! Oh, Marsha!" Tears of happiness welled up in Mrs. Hoyt's eyes.

"That's very generous," said Marsha.

Eldon Hoyt spoke up for the first time. "The money is not the main consideration. We want Marsha to keep on with her singing, certainly, but she's a big girl now and has to make up her own mind on things."

His wife glared at him. "Eldon! Marsha would be out of her mind not to jump at this chance to be a great star."

"It's nice of you to remember me all these years, Mr. Goodman," said Marsha with a smile. "And to come way out to Rockfort to see me. But I need time to think about such a drastic change in my life. I'm happy here. I'm satisfied. It'd be a big change."

Goodman drew from his pocket a sheaf of papers. "I have a contract here, and will leave it with you." He edged forward on the sofa, placed the contract on the coffee table, and raised himself up with effort.

"You'll be singing Romberg, Berlin, Kern, Rodgers and Hart, and Porter. It's a great opportunity. I hope you'll consider it seriously, Miss Hoyt."

"I will, Mr. Goodman. Thank you. I appreciate your kindness."

"Our offer is good for a week. Here's my card. Give me a call when you decide."

Mrs. Hoyt broke into tears and rushed upstairs as Marsha and her father showed Ace Goodman to the door.

In her room, alone, Marsha puzzled over the almost eerie timing. Only hours after the pact she had made with Ginny, a strange man offers a glamorous new career. Show business. Fame, money, new friends, her name suddenly known to millions.

If Mr. Goodman had come along a month ago, would she have accepted the offer? She might be in New York now, doing test shots, learning new songs, selecting wardrobe. Her mother would be deliriously happy. The ladies of the garden club would receive the latest bulletin on Marsha Hoyt's progress and the Rockfort *Daily News* would write about how it feels when a local artist moves into the big time.

Maybe her mother and Goodman were right. How many church singers ever got a chance to be on national television? Her college friends would be astounded if she hesitated for five minutes before taking the job. The college shows had been exciting. Packed houses. Applause. Praise. In those days she hadn't thought too much about a professional career. But now—?

Was it to be New York or her new-found life in following Jesus? Leap into the whirl of show business? Or be one of the leaders in Willard Merrill's exciting new plan?

As if on cue, her mother appeared. "Marsha, I shouldn't have run out like that. Not saying goodbye to Mr. Goodman. But I was so upset. Just the thought of you not taking this wonderful opportunity! Why it's unbelievable! I know you have plans at the church, but you can't let that interfere with your career! This is the chance of a lifetime. You'll never get a better offer. Just think of it! Hollywood!"

"Mom, I know what you're saying. It's a marvelous offer. But, I—"

"You can't refuse it. Do you want to be stuck here in Rockfort all your life? Singing in a church? You'll never meet anyone here. You have to get out in the world with important people. Men with big positions, executives—"

"But, there's more to life than that!"

"You're so stubborn! I've said all I am going to say. Do as you please. Stay in your little rut. But don't forget this, your father and I have done everything in the world for you. And we don't deserve this!"

She stormed out of the room and Marsha buried her face as the tears came. Slowly, she undressed and prepared for a shower. But the relaxation that usually came with the pleasing hot spray eluded her.

That evening, the subject of television was not mentioned at dinner. The half hour was strained, dotted with small talk that pretended to be important and failed dismally.

Marsha spent the evening in her room. She tried to sort out her life. Yesterday, meeting with Ginny. Their enthusiasm for the new program. Helping in new ways. A totally new direction in life. To live as Jesus would live! To do as He would do! Not simply another cause, another committee formed to raise funds, another busload of under-privileged children taken on a trip to a museum with a stop at a lakeside resort. It was much larger than that.

And her word. She had entered a pact with Ginny. But Ginny would understand. Willard would understand. Her father would understand.

For most of the night she tossed in her bed. Cameras, bright lights, more money than she had ever dreamed of. She visualized new faces, new opportunities. She saw Willard Merrill standing in his pulpit. She saw him facing the congregation at church; there was the agonized expression of the young man who had died; Ginny and her great desire to share.

Sometime just before dawn the familiar words of a hymn ran through her thoughts. *Awake My Soul, Away My Fear. I'll Mount Above My Tiring Load.* The words kept repeating themselves, over and over again. Finally, moments before falling into deep slumber, she spoke aloud: Give me the courage, Lord, to take the right road. Jesus help me.

6

It was an ordinary Monday morning for most employees at the County Trust Company but the president, Rodney Brent, felt a touch of indigestion as he looked over the bank's inventory of major loans—those of $2 million or more.

The list was long and far too many were in question. Loans to farm owners hurt by low prices and over-supply. Loans extended, on the urging of larger banks, to oil and gas ventures in the Southwest. Loans to heavy industry—companies still struggling to come back from years of red ink.

Only Rodney Brent, two senior officers of the bank and various federal bank regulators knew the true story. The bank's percentage of loans to assets, if the bad risks were recognized as such, was horrendous. If half of the bad risks were written off, the bank's profits would vanish. There would be a huge deficit for the year. And when there's a deficit, shareholders sell their stock, depositors withdraw their funds.

Brent did not appreciate a visit from Mal Goodenough, his trust officer. The man, chubby and bald, had an annoying habit of blinking constantly. "Rod, were you at church yesterday?"

The president nodded.

"Is the story true? That a lot of people are going to live the way Jesus would?"

There was no reply.

"Thought I'd ask. Know it's your church. Funny how word

like this gets around. I thought at least—"

"I'm busy now, Mal."

"Sure. Sorry." Mal hurried away, mumbling, "That Merrill must be a weirdo."

It was worse during lunch at the City Club. Rod Brent was part of the Pleasant Valley Church. A generous supporter. A trustee. As cynics had observed, it was good business to be identified with the church. With so many successful business-men as parishioners, a well-dressed assortment of Rockfort's shrewd bankers, insurance salesmen and other peddlers of financial instruments were seen at church regularly.

The jibes were relentless.

"Rod, when are you going to start dressing in sackcloth and sandals?"

"You won't be able to turn down a loan applicant now, Rod. 'Do unto others!' Right?"

On and on. Brent was in no mood for their banter. He was depressed. The bank's problems had never been as worri-some. After a while the club members tired of the fun and Rod Brent went back to his office. But it was the same later in the day at cocktail hour. Nothing about the Middle East, the stock market, interest rates. Instead, the new Jesus move-ment was the club's topic of the day. Like a juicy scandal, it involved people, local people and their individual doings, the stuff that makes gossip, rumor, speculation. The men at the club loved to vie with one another to come up with witty re-marks. After one drink, Brent left, saying he had dinner guests, which was a lie.

Driving home alone in his Continental, Rod Brent glowered and then sighed. That damn Merrill. What's he think he's doing? He's got this whole town riled up.

7
—————

All week, despite moments of doubt and concern, Willard Merrill had tried to be optimistic about his new program. After all his years of searching, Merrill had discovered, finally, what Jesus wanted him to do.

Follow Me! Do as I taught you to do!

Now, alone in his study on Saturday morning, preparing to write his Sunday sermon, he suddenly was engulfed in waves of uncertainty.

The minister's face was grave. What was he doing to these people? Could they, in their everyday lives, really do as Jesus would do? It was one thing for a church leader to set forth a new program and ask that it be rigidly adhered to. It was quite another to expose those you care most about to dissension, strife, outright hostility.

His own home was a glaring example. Ann, the finest wife a man could have, was in sharp disagreement with the Jesus idea. It was their first serious rift in 30 years. How far was he prepared to go if it meant endangering his marriage? Ann would not change her mind. He knew her too well. She was intelligent, spirited, practical. Her staunch Yankee background made her see things as they were. Ann was no dreamer.

Ann's family had been moderately well to do. She was accustomed to nice things. In Merrill's early ministry, things had not been easy for Ann. Budgets, usually meager, had been a constant concern. Only with the move to Rockfort ten years ago had the Pleasant Valley Church provided an above-average income and a fine residence to go with it.

Ann loved her home. She liked things to run smoothly, to harmonize; she studiously avoided situations that might "upset things." Willard Merrill knew this and he was aware that new ideas, if pursued, could be highly disruptive. He also knew there was no turning back. No forgetting last Sunday and the first meeting. No abandoning the pledges, the dedication of his group.

He took a pencil and wrote a name on a pad.

Ed Vernon.

Immediate problems with key aides. Editors, department heads, those on the business side. How far was Vernon prepared to go? Suppose the worst happened. Substantial loss of readership and circulation. A drop in advertising income. Lay-offs. Increasing pressure from the competition. Ed Vernon was Merrill's close friend and a fine man but what of his obligations to his staff? To his family? To his heirs?

A newspaper, more than most services, was highly vulner-able to public opinion. Rockfort had radio, television, another daily paper. No one *had* to buy the *News*. Publishing was not like running a bus line or providing electricity. Ed Vernon was at high risk.

Don Turner.

Only yesterday, Don had called. His two star salesmen had quit, joined a rival dealership down the Boulevard. The word was unsettling to Merrill. Don was friendly, outgoing, capable. In the new program, he would be in church regularly. And Sara Turner was one of the hard workers in the church. Merrill knew she backed her husband. But did she have any idea of the potential harm to his three dealerships?

Merrill didn't want Don Turner to have a bad time. It was that simple. And yet—the commitment was made. There was no turning back.

Wes McLain.

Wes was in many respects the most dedicated of all. A lover of the Bible. The Word of Jesus. His wife and son were ridicul-ing him. His employees were in revolt.

What if there was a strike? It was threatened. What if Wes lost his job? That was possible. Could Wes McLain con-tinue on course, with Jesus? That was the pledge he had taken. And he, Merrill, was responsible.

Marsha and Virginia.

When they came to see him on Friday, they had already been blessed with a spiritual idea. They were dedicated, en-thused, utterly sincere. They wanted to do more than just help. They wanted a project, something in the community to give real meaning to the pledge—to do as Jesus would do. They were every bit as committed as Merrill himself.

He could count on these two gracious, lovely young women no matter how difficult things became. While they hadn't complained, Merrill knew their families were totally opposed to their involvement. The minister thanked God for Marsha and Virginia. Then he shook his head in concern for what they might be called to endure.

Rodney Brent.

The most powerful man in Rockfort, a supporter of the church. Brent had labeled the entire idea as nonsense. Merrill was crazy, no doubt about it.

The minister rose from his desk and paced the floor. Was he harming people? Upsetting their lives? Was it right to cause such turmoil? Perhaps he, Willard Merrill, was wrong. Perhaps no one today could run his life as Jesus had done two thousand years ago. Was it a mistake to try?

Willard Merrill fell to his knees and prayed aloud.

Jesus, help me. I know I am right in seeking to follow Thee. The way is clear, the path is open. Your divine inspiration leads and directs my every move. There is no other way.

He opened his Book to the 18th Psalm:1, 2. Slowly he read *I will love Thee, O Lord, my strength. The Lord is my rock, and my fortress, and my deliverer; my God, my strength, in whom I will trust.* Merrill paused. It is all right there, he told himself. Everything I could possibly need or use. To love God can only mean living and acting in a Godly manner. What else?

Then it must be clear that God, as my strength, my rock, my fortress, is equal to any situation. When I trust in that strength, completely, my victory is assured. There is no other meaning to the Psalm.

For a long time he meditated, knowing the truth of what he had declared. Slowly, he felt his anxiety begin to lift. He became aware of renewed energy, of a new sense of calm, of peace. He closed his eyes and let the Holy Spirit descend and enfold him, imparting fresh strength and vigor. He gave himself totally to a realization of a new inner security. In that moment he knew he never again would doubt the clear course that had been revealed to him. Jesus taught that the problem and the solution are always within.

Can I believe that the power within me will triumph? Yes. And I do not merely hope, I have faith. I do not think "perhaps." I know. Jesus said: *As within, so without.* We will go forward, on our course.

The minister rose, stood tall; on his handsome face was resolution. He went to his desk and began to write his sermon.

At dinner, Ann brought a casserole in from the kitchen and sat opposite her husband. "Will, you've had a busy week. It's been good to see you like your old self again. Did you finish your sermon for tomorrow?"

"Yes."

"What's it on?"

"Believing in Jesus, what he taught. Following Him. His way. Praying to Him. If people would do this they'd overcome all obstacles. Our work here—our main job—is to live as Jesus would—"

"Willard! Are you going to persist in that notion? I thought by now you'd see how impossible your idea is. Why, you'll turn this church inside out if you keep on! Can't you see that?"

"Quite the contrary."

Ann frowned. "I can't believe this! If you'd heard what I heard this week, you'd come to your senses. Fast. Everywhere, people ask what's going on at the church. They have funny looks on their faces."

"Ann, it's the way to go, the only way."

Ann Merrill pushed her chair back from the table. "Willard, I beg you to wait. Put it off for a month and see how you feel later on." She rose and came around to him and put her arm around his shoulder. "Darling, you've been carried away by

69

this whole thing. It all started with that young man. But don't push too hard. Postpone the idea. You can patch up your sermon and take the sticky parts out. In time, you'll see what I mean."

She moved toward the door.

He rose from the table. "Don't worry, honey, things will work out. Stormy weather, maybe. But we'll survive." He started toward her, arms outstretched. She turned away and went into the kitchen.

8

Sunday morning the ushers carried folding chairs up from Activities in an effort to seat everyone. It was not enough. This was the biggest turnout ever at the Pleasant Valley Church. Many elected to stand at the rear; others reluctantly returned to their cars.

The regulars were seated well before eleven. They had anticipated a big crowd. Marsha's first hymn, by Horatius Bonar, conveyed to some a hint of Merrill's theme for the day.

I heard the voice of Jesus say,
"I am this dark world's light;
Look unto Me, thy moon shall rise,
And all thy day be bright."
I looked to Jesus, and I found
In Him my start, my sun;
And in that light of life I'll walk
Till traveling days are done.

Willard Merrill could pick out those in his central group— Ed Vernon, Wes McLain, Don Turner, Virginia—and it was comforting to see the support, the interest, the sincerity reflected in their expressions. The minister knew he was not alone. It did not disturb him when his eyes picked up, one by one, the critical who were so ready to scorn, to ridicule. Rodney Brent, Grace Hoyt, Gerald Carver and Aunt Geraldine, Mrs. Oswald Yorke.

70

In his opening remarks, Merrill commented on the swirl of notoriety surrounding the church during the week.

"We seem to have made some news. And I'm confident it's for the good. Welcome to all of you who are here for the first time, and welcome to those who've been away from us for a while. To you I quote I Kings 13:7: *Come home with Me and refresh yourself.*"

Just before his announcements, Merrill decided he would not look at Ann during the service. He knew she was upset. It would distract him to see her anxiety. He spotted Wes McLain with his wife and he wondered why Alice McLain had come on this particular Sunday. Was it curiosity? Wanting to be there in case something dramatic occurred? Not far from the McLain's were Rod Brent and his daughter, Judy. Brent's jowly features revealed his feelings: This is boring and it's hogwash but I'm here anyway. Good business to be seen in church.

Merrill plunged into his sermon. "We have but one job, one work to perform. Believe in Jesus and His way. Then all else will follow: health, joy, our material needs, accomplishments in our careers. Above all, peace."

As the minister warmed to his subject, the audience before him became a blur. No longer was there an impulse to identify individuals. His delivery grew in intensity; his voice gathered strength with each phrase, his steady blue eyes riveted on one section of the auditorium, then another. His exultant face glowed as he spoke.

"We must become the servants of Jesus Christ. Doing His will in every act of our lives. We must ask ourselves the question: Are we really Christians or are we something else? If we are true Christians, doing the work of Jesus, then it must be all or nothing. There are no half measures in the teachings of Jesus. Can we imagine exercising an option to do as Jesus would do *only* when we felt like it? And doing something else at other times? Consider our fundamental commandment—*Love one another*...as we know it in John:13:34. Are

71

we to obey it only when we feel like it? And at other times ignore it, and indulge in selfishness, malice, hatred? Of course not!"

Merrill pointed out that the Bible emphasizes over and over again the need to run our lives according to the teachings of Jesus. And it all starts within us. "We need look no further than Luke, 17:21: *The Kingdom of God is within you.* Is there anything in this life, anywhere in the world, to equal that phrase? If we could have but one thing in our lives it would be the knowledge that the Kingdom of God is within us! God is within us all the time, hoping to be heard. We are not to reject Him with sinful actions, negative thoughts about others. Greed—give me *more!* Selfishness—I come *first!* We can't have God within us and ignore the sin that is all around us. We can't have God within us and isolate ourselves in secluded, comfortable surroundings, safe from troubles outside, aloof from the needs of our fellows. If God is within us, then our proper course is to follow Jesus, do as Jesus would do. Not just for an hour on Sunday mornings but all the time. God within means kindness in dealing with our neighbor. It means honesty in our dealings in business. It means rejecting sin of all kinds, helping those who are living in sin. God within means Love!"

The minister explained that by following Jesus, we are to think before speaking and acting. We are to ask ourselves, what would Jesus do? What would He say? Merrill then described the new group formed at the church. Its goals. Its guidelines. He invited all to join, explaining there were weekly meetings but none of the usual committees, officers or dues. It was all voluntary. He closed by reading the sixth and seventh verses of Psalm 95:6-7. *O come, let us worship and bow down: let us kneel before the Lord our Maker. For He is our God; and we are the people of His pasture.*

It was an inspired sermon. The buzz of comments in the lobby was more vigorous than usual. Outside the church, Grace Hoyt cornered Ann Merrill.

"My dear, you simply have to do something. Why doesn't

this notion of the Reverend's go away? He's had a week to come to his senses!"

Before Ann could reply, they were joined by Mrs. Oswald Yorke, regal in a deep-green flowered dress and a white straw hat, and by Geraldine Carver and Jerry Carver.

"Does this mean we have to find another church?" Geraldine asked. "How welcome will we be if we don't join the club?"

"That's silly," Ann said quickly. "Willard's not stupid."

"He's become a crusader," Jerry Carver replied.

Grace Hoyt spoke up. "Everybody's confused. They don't know what he's talking about. How can everybody be like Jesus? Act like Him? Today? Ridiculous!"

"I think our good minister needs his vacation," Geraldine Carver observed. "It's next month, isn't it?"

"August," Ann said.

"Keep him out of the sun," Jerry advised.

"This enormous crowd!" Grace Hoyt complained. "People I don't even know. Where did they come from?"

"What are they doing in *our* church?" asked Mrs. Yorke. "Nothing like a scandal to attract just anybody!"

"It's *not* a scandal," Ann said, visibly shaken. "If you'll all just be patient, things will settle down."

"Yes, and when the sideshow is over, when they've had their laughs, this church will be empty! People are not fools. Impersonate Jesus! What nonsense!" Mrs. Yorke stomped away.

Ann frowned and hurried off, only to be surrounded by others before she could re-enter the church. Similar reactions, some milder, others downright sarcastic, peppered her until at last she escaped and made her way down to Activities. The meeting was already under way.

Merrill outlined to newcomers the vows the Followers of Jesus had taken. He explained how the program was to work and what was expected of participants. He saw no reason to avoid the negatives. "It hasn't been easy for us, at our jobs or at home." He pointed to Wes McLain. "Wes, would you tell us how things are with you?"

Wes McLain rose and faced the others. "I was, quite honestly, shocked by what happened in my own family. Absolutely no understanding. No interest. They made fun of the whole idea. But I can tell you this. It only proves to me how much I need Jesus. For His help. For strength. People need Him today more than ever. But they fight Him, and what He stands for. My dear Mother would've been all-out for us. But she's long gone."

Ed Vernon's hand went up.

"I don't mind saying it's tough at the paper. Luckily, my family is with me a hundred percent. But I can't find anyone on the job who isn't either scornful of what we're doing or afraid of how it'll affect them, or both."

Willard Merrill asked: "What do they actually fear, Ed?"

"Less overtime, fewer pay raises, even loss of their jobs."

Don Turner spoke up. "It's tough going over at my place. As Ed says, people are afraid to follow Jesus. His Way of thinking and acting is contrary to everything they know, everything they've been taught."

A hand went up from one of the newcomers. "Mr. Vernon, if your business is in trouble, and yours too, Mr. Turner, how do you see this program working? Won't we all have the same kind of trouble?"

Vernon and Turner looked at Reverend Merrill, and the minister took the challenge. "We must begin by knowing the rightness of our actions. We are not inventing a new religious movement. We are simply going according to Bible teachings. How can we be wrong if we follow Jesus, the Greatest Teacher who ever lived? Look around you. What do you see? A world that is sick. Crime, wars, starvation. Cheating, dishonesty, corruption. People obsessed with sex, addicted to drugs, alcohol. Families failing—divorce mounting. Morally, we are at the lowest ebb since before the fall of Rome. If we in this church can become the leaders in spreading the idea of doing as Jesus would do—in every situation regardless of the cost—many lives will be transformed. The world *will* be made better!"

A half hour later, after six newcomers to the group had taken their pledges, the meeting ended. The group appeared to be deeply affected, with determination and enthusiasm masking whatever doubts they may have had. All knelt and the minister led them in prayer for guidance, strength and harmony as they began their new lives.

9

That evening was a difficult time at the parsonage.

"Willard," Ann said solemnly. "I'm trying to understand you, and I'm getting nowhere. I'm afraid for you. For us. Don't you see where all this can lead? What it could do to us?"

"It'll work out, dear."

"But it can't! You have a handful of people willing to go along with you. To start. Do you think for one minute they'll do this thing for more than a week or two? They'll drop out. They'll have to!"

"No one said it'd be easy."

"It'll be a catastrophe, Willard. Wait till their families and people in their offices find out what's really going on. I could tell from the things Ed Vernon and Don Turner said, and that nice Mr. McLain. They're putting up a brave front now. Sure, it's only been a week or so. But you can't live today the way people did back then. I can't for the life of me understand how you can let that drifter change our lives."

"He was just a part of it. A trigger you might say."

"If only he hadn't come near our church!" Ann went on, her voice rising. "Why couldn't he have gone to some other church where the minister would've said, 'I'm sorry' and then forgotten about it?"

"It wasn't to be."

"Will, you're in some sort of fog. You simply *have* to snap out of it. You've worked so hard. All those years we did without things. Here in Rockfort, at last we have something. Don't you see you could lose your congregation over this nonsense? You could lose your job!"

"Highly unlikely."

"You're impossible!" Tears starting, Ann rushed up the stairs.

He watched her go, sighed, and went to his study. He knelt and tried to pray for guidance. In his great sadness and distress the best he could do was to repeat over and over again the third verse of the 23rd Psalm. *He restoreth my soul, He leadeth me in the path of righteousness for His name's sake.*

Willard Merrill's mind was in turmoil.

Later, when he finally went upstairs and eased quietly into bed, Ann was asleep. Throughout most of the night the minister tossed and turned. The events of the past two weeks whirled in his head. Repeatedly, in his agony, he asked himself if he and his wonderful followers could actually live as Jesus would live. Do as He would do. Is it possible today? Or would they have to relent, acknowledge defeat? The minister was certain of one thing: he could never give up his new program and remain in Rockfort. The humiliation, the shame would be too much. He would be compelled to resign.

He struggled to put aside his fear. In desperation, he fought to think only of Jesus, of the pledge to Him. He forced himself to believe that he was right.

Dawn was breaking when sleep finally came.

10

Dana Bell waited until Ed Vernon was alone, then he walked determinedly into the publisher's office and closed the door.

"The news dealers are complaining," Bell said gloomily. "Griping about what's missing in the paper. Their customers are yelling. The paper's gotten dull!"

"We expected it," Vernon said easily.

"The reporters are unhappy," Bell went on. "They think if we pass up crime and everything with violence we'll lose circulation and they'll lose their jobs."

Vernon motioned Bell to a chair. "We've no plans for any layoffs, Dana."

"Not yet. But if we drop a lot of stuff they buy the paper for, it's only a matter of time. Advertising is worried. Watkins said this morning the first four contracts he cancelled brought howls you could hear all the way to South Bend. Three liquor stores, the race track and the x-rated movie house."

"We'll replace that business."

"That's a tall order, Ed, if circulation continues to drop. Our returns from dealers are way up. No cancellations of home deliveries yet; it's too early for that."

When Vernon was silent, Bell continued: "Even a ten percent drop in readership and we got to drop ad rates ten percent. Can't do it. Our margin's too tight."

Bell got nowhere. Vernon would not back down. Amiable, generous, understanding, Ed Vernon also had a reputation for dogged persistence, outright stubborness. Dana Bell shook his head and went back to his office.

Vernon could not remain at his desk. He was edgy, nervous. When three calls to Willard Merrill brought busy signals, the publisher went out to his car. Before he started the engine, he prayed. It cannot be this bad, he told himself. We are right, I know we are right. God give me the strength to follow Jesus, to do as He would do.

In spite of his prayers, Ed Vernon's tension remained. He was more uncertain of his new course than at any time since taking the pledge. He could not go home. He did not want to be alone. Barbara was at her mother's in Glendon. Hildy was on a day-long camping trip. Would there be a kindred soul, a sympathetic ear at the City Club? The most unlikely place but a few members were long-time friends; they might not agree with Merrill's new program but they'd understand. They'd listen and perhaps do no more than express their skepticism.

It was not to be.

"What's happened to your paper, Ed?" was the opening shot from the local manager for a large insurance company. "It's gotten dull."

"Hey Ed," a contractor said. "What gives? No results from the track! Is this Merrill's doing? I had the daily double yesterday. Had to buy a St. Louis paper to find out."

Rockfort's best divorce lawyer chimed in. "Ed's smart. He's got a plan. He's going to turn the *News* into the *Daily New Testament News!*"

Vernon tried to smile, to be good-natured but he soon gave up and left the club. Slowly he began the 10-minute drive to his home. Anxiety at the paper. Ridicule and scorn at the club. Where were his real friends? The *News* could go out of business and City Club members would line up at the bar and say what a shame it was. Then they'd talk about money and women.

Ed Vernon drove into his garage and shut off the engine but he made no move to get out. He bowed his head, resting on his arms circling the steering wheel. Can I really do it? Can I run the *News* as Jesus would? I love that paper. Maybe I've never admitted to myself how much I love the *News*. What would I do if it went under?

He sat erect. No! I block these thoughts as they try to enter my consciousness. I turn to Jesus. I place my faith in Him. Merrill is certain we can do it. I believe in him.

If I believe enough, the *News* cannot fail.

11

It was after ten in the evening when the headlights of a car swept across the big picture window at Don and Sara Turner's home.

Don went to the front door to admit Jed Benson, his sales manager.

"Sorry to barge in like this, Don," Benson said. "But you'll be over at Eastside tomorrow and I must talk with you."

They went into Turner's pine-panelled den and Benson took a large sheet of white paper from his pocket. "Since we pulled our ads to rewrite the copy—I have the figures right here—showroom traffic is off twenty-two percent. The new ad ran today. It pulled nothing!"

"I realize that."

"Sales this month will be lower. A year ago, we did a hundred and eighteen units. We'll be lucky to hit eighty. The whole industry is up and we'll be down!"

"Not for long."

"I'm surprised you'd say that, Don. You know this business better than anyone. We're moving down, and we'll keep sliding with this Jesus idea of yours. Service is teed off. Their hourly time is down because one service worker is following your idea. He's dragging his two teams down and the guys don't like it."

"Sam told me he'd go along."

"He's crazy! The technicians will gripe to factory service reps. Then we got trouble. And that won't be all. Wait 'til factories take a look at sales. These franchises are not yours for a lifetime. You know that, Don."

"Yes."

Jed Benson cited more reasons why Turner should abandon his silly ideas about God and Jesus before any more damage could be done. The more he talked, the more defensive Don Turner became. At eleven o'clock, Jed abruptly rose and walked out of the house without a word to his employer.

Sara had gone to bed. Don didn't wish to involve her in the turmoil that was fast getting out of hand. He hoped she wouldn't call him or come downstairs.

Why is the right way so difficult? he asked himself. You'd think doing business honestly would be refreshingly easy. But it wasn't. Greed was in control. Make the buck no matter what you have to do. The name of the game is profit and nothing else is important.

His three franchises were extremely valuable—and vulnerable. When a dealer does poorly at a time when everyone else is doing well, he's in trouble. A manufacturer always has another dealer, well-financed, waiting to take over a prized franchise. The sales reps, on their regular visits from district offices, were Turner's friends—for as long as things prospered.

Don Turner tried to pray. His thoughts were blurred and his head ached. He opened the Bible and came upon a line in 2 Timothy 1:7. *For God hath not given us the spirit of fear, but of power, and of love, and of a sound mind.* He stared at the words for a long time, reading them half-aloud, over and over again.

He slumped down on the sofa. Sometime after midnight, he fell into a deep sleep beset with agonizing dreams.

12

They stormed Wes McLain's office just before lunch break. Rollie Makin and Bo Stacy, the head checkers, came first, followed by Jim Akers, the superintendent. They formed a belligerent semi-circle in front of McLain's cluttered desk.

Makin was the union shop steward at East-West Lines. He blurted out his views in a high-pitched, whiney voice.

"It's no go, Mr. McLain. The drivers won't buy it, the loaders won't buy it. As head checkers here, me and Bo ain't buyin' it. You can't make us pay for merchandise that ain't on the rigs. We can't double-check every crate, every box. Not and make the schedules."

"Stealing has to stop," McLain said quietly.

"It ain't stopped before for more'n a week at a time. We got no control over what a driver does on the road."

"Look," McLain said. "A driver picks up in Denver. He's supposed to check every item before he signs the bill. When he drops along the way, he checks off each time. What's so hard about keeping control of what he's carrying? Why can't he arrive at Columbus with an exact count?"

"It don't work so easy, Mr. McLain," said Stacy. "He drops ten boxes and he may pick up five. He can make six or a dozen stops in two days. It's the computers; they screw things up. It ain't us."

"All I know is, the insurance companies are getting tougher every day," McLain continued. "They say our records are in bad shape. They say we got no control at all over theft because we don't use the safeguards we have."

Jim Akers took a short step forward, as if it was his turn. "What they're trying to say, Wes, is that this thing spreads over a lot of guys in a lot of places. We don't have electric eyes watching every point coast to coast."

"I realize that, Jim," Wes McLain said sharply. "But the fact remains that with proper checking we can reduce theft of merchandise ticketed through this terminal by at least fifty percent. We're too easy. We're too sloppy. And it's got to stop. You men can make it stop!

Makin's face reddened. "You callin' us crooks, Mr. McLain?"

McLain's voice rose. "I'm not calling anybody anything—not just yet."

"It sure sounds like it."

"If you want to see it that way, that's your choice."

"I don't like being called a thief."

Suddenly McLain pounded his desk and half rose from his chair. "I'm going to run an honest operation here."

"You don't know what goes on!" Makin shouted back. "You ain't on the platforms. You're here in your easy chair."

"Take it easy, Rollie," Stacy said.

"I won't take it easy! Nobody's crappin' me about missin' stuff I don't know nuthin' about!"

Jim Akers put a hand on Makin's shoulder and pulled him back. "Let's go."

"Damn right we'll go!"

Akers struggled briefly with Makin and forced him back to the door while McLain advanced on the men. Makin shouted.

"Lousy, fouled up joint!"

"All right, all right," Akers said firmly and tried to pull Makin to the door.

Suddenly McLain straightened, turned slowly away from them. His face mirrored the thought: What would Jesus do? He went to the window and stared out at the rows of trucks at the loading bays. Jesus would be calm, first of all. He would pray. McLain tried to form words of prayer. His lips moved almost imperceptively: Jesus help me. I believe. Jesus, Savior, be my strength. I have faith. You are my life.

When he turned back, the men had gone. He hadn't heard them leave.

13

Grace Hoyt's footsteps had a familiar ring. They clattered sharply now in the lower hall, echoing impatience and determination. Marsha knew only too well that an invasion of her room was seconds away. For days she had struggled with Goodman's offer.

It was a wonderful offer. Every church soloist, every college show star would jump at the chance. New York, Hollywood. Television; films, perhaps. Lunch at Sardi's in New York, dinner at Chasen's in Hollywood. Of her ability, Marsha was confident. She had studied, worked hard on her tonal qualities, her enunciation, her accenting. She had no fear of failure.

What held her back? She had struggled to put her life in focus. Basically somewhat shy, Marsha had been frozen with fear before her first stage entrance in every college show. Once on stage, she had always been able to lose herself in her role and perform with distinction.

Why, then, had this success failed to send her off to Broadway? Thousands of less talented hopefuls made the trip every year.

Marsha loved her work at the church. It was as satisfying as singing the lead in *Kiss Me, Kate.* And she had grown in consciousness under the teachings of Willard Merrill. Fears, doubts, self-criticism, periods of depression—all the familiar emotions that cloud our lives—had been present in Marsha's early life; they had all but vanished after she started working and singing at the church. She awoke each day with enthusiasm, energy. She was active, cheerful.

Marsha Hoyt was a happy person.

"Marsha," her mother said, sweeping in majestically without waiting for her knock at the door to be answered. "Have you made up your mind? Mr. Goodman's in town. He called when you were out. He wants your decision. For you to delay like this is so stubborn and foolish!"

"Mother, I haven't made a final decision."

Her mother glared at her. "I've said my last word on the subject." She turned to go. "You do as you please, as usual!"

Marsha knew she had to get out of the house. It was a

beautiful day. She went out through a side door, crossed the broad lawn and began the mile walk to Virginia Carver's home. She tried to breathe deeply, to clear her mind. One thing was certain. She had to decide. She couldn't keep Mr. Goodman waiting any longer.

"What do you think I should do?" she asked Virginia. Geraldine Carver, sitting in a far corner of the room, looked at a magazine and pretended not to hear.

"Marsh," Virginia said softly. "It's a big decision. Terribly important. Your whole life is on the line." She looked away thoughtfully. "I wouldn't dream of advising you. It's something only you can decide, by yourself."

"You're a big help."

Virginia smiled. "It's either take the job or not."

Geraldine looked up suddenly. "Of course you should take it! Are you crazy?"

Try as she would, Marsha could get no advice from Virginia. After a while, Jerry Carver appeared and when Marsha stood up to leave he invited himself to walk home with her.

"I guess you'll be heading for the big-time?" Jerry said.

"It's a very flattering offer. My mother thinks I'm insane not to leap at it. Your aunt feels the same way."

"How do you feel?"

Marsha paused, and then she said: "I'm wavering. Right now I'm in the middle. But I'm happy right here at home."

"Could I try to sway you?"

"Why not?

"It's selfish, I guess," he said hesitantly. "But I'd vote for you to stay put."

"Why?"

Jerry smiled. "Because—I'm very fond of you."

When she was silent, he went on. "If you decided to stay in Rockfort, I'd be the happiest guy around."

"Thank you."

"I want you to stay, Marsha, because—I'm in love with you."

Marsha stopped walking and looked at him. "Jerry."

"It's the truth."

It was her turn to search for words. "I've never thought about you in that way."

"I mean it."

"I believe you, Jerry." She smiled faintly. "Right now I really don't know how I feel about you and—"

"You might change."

The words rushed out. "Ever since I've known you, you've been Rockfort's man about town. The easy life. You live for your own enjoyment without much interest in anyone else. I guess I'm old-fashioned. But that's not the sort of life I—I value."

When he didn't reply, she continued. "That's rude of me. I'm sorry. I've no right to criticize you. Everyone should live as they want, I suppose."

They walked in silence. At her home, a pensive Jerry said goodbye.

Marsha, already disturbed by Jerry's expressed feelings, was unprepared for the next surprise. Her mother and Ace Goodman were standing in the center of the living room.

They exchanged awkard greetings.

Marsha Hoyt's voice was firm, clear. "I think I've just about made up my mind, Mr. Goodman. I'll never be able to thank you enough for your kindness, but I want to stay in Rockfort."

Before Grace Hoyt could speak, Marsha turned and hurried out to the hall and up the stairs. Goodman ran after her.

"Marsha, please think it over," he called out." We can improve the offer—"

Goodman heard the door to her room close and turned back to Mrs. Hoyt.

"It's that Merrill!"she said acidly. "He's the one. She'd never in the world turn this down on her own."

"You mean, he advised her?"

"No, no! It's his new Jesus program. She's fallen for it, hook, line and sinker!"

"I see."

"I can tell you, the man's a menace to the community. He's got some fine people trapped in this thing. You wouldn't believe what's going on!"

Goodman made no reply. He seemed lost in thought.

"The very idea of Marsha—" Grace Hoyt began.

"Wait! I have an idea. If this minister's so powerful, maybe we can use him."

"What?"

"Let's use the guy. If he has so much influence over her, maybe he can get her to sign."

"Don't be ridiculous!"

"Not at all." He smiled knowingly. "These guys are nothing but fund-raisers at heart. A little gift—cash, that is—to his church and I guarantee he'll be on our side."

For once in her life, Grace Hoyt was speechless.

August

1

Rodney Brent stalled as long as he could, then he walked slowly to the large conference room where the bank's directors were waiting. He had dreaded the session since an early morning call from Cleveland.

"I thought I better reach you before your meeting today, Rod. It didn't work out with the takeover deal. And there's nothing new anywhere. We can't make the payment today."

It was one more blow, one more bad loan to be written off, one step more on the County Trust Company's road to disaster. Brent tried to appear calm.

Would he tell them? Or hold off for a while? Something might happen. A bright spot might shine through the dark clouds. He smiled grimly. Very unlikely. Conservatively, a bank should loan out no more than 63% of its deposits. At County Trust, loans came to an alarming 92% of deposits.

He greeted the directors and called the meeting to order.

The secretary read the minutes of the previous week's meeting. The treasurer brought the balance sheet up to date. Then the chief loan officer was asked for his report. It was bad.

"As of the first of the month, three of our biggest loans are now regarded as in default. According to Federal Reserve rules, we must write down a portion of that, an additional twenty-two million."

The directors were stunned.

"We can't do that!" one said.

"Impossible!" another cried.

"What about Smithson in Texas? Demand payment from them!"

"They're in bankruptcy."

A murky silence fell over the group. Rodney Brent knew that mention of the morning's news from Cleveland would mean panic. He guided the discussion to the less severe bad-loan situations. Gradually, the questions shifted to profits.

"What are we looking at for the second quarter?" a director asked.

The treasurer shuffled some papers. "With these new write-downs, let's see." His pencil raced over a yellow pad while the directors stared at him. Finally, he said: "Perhaps ten cents a share."

"What!" a director exploded. "That's down from forty-eight cents the last quarter!"

"And for the third quarter," the treasurer intoned, "adjusted, we can see a loss of twenty-cents."

Through the uproar that followed, Rodney Brent sat quietly and watched them squirm. Except for four officers of County Trust, they were leaders in law, industry, retailing. And they were facing a crisis. They had their own incomes but they all owned significant amounts of stock in the bank.

"We must stretch out these loans," an attorney said. "Extend our deadlines."

"It's easier to stretch out a loan to Argentina than one to Franklin Tool."

"Nonsense!"

"It's a fact."

Rodney Brent rapped on the table and said: "We have to face the reality of the write-offs. The quality of our earnings is bound to suffer. Bank stocks are supposed to be relatively stable. If we drop anywhere near the figures suggested here this morning, we'll be in trouble with our stock. The big share-holders—Hobart Varney, for example, and Mary Reese—won't sit by and watch us drop ten, or even five dollars a share. They'll sell. I don't have to tell you what that will mean. We're not Chase Manhattan. We're a small bank."

"I've got news for you," a manufacturing executive said. "The Investment Fund at the college and Mid-West Insurance will sell a lot sooner than old Hobart Varney. Those guys move fast."

"How long before any public announcement?" the lawyer asked.

The treasurer answered: "Our second quarter earnings are due September fifteenth."

"That's six weeks. Something may happen."

After more head-shaking, discussions of possible remedies for the problem and predictions of inevitable catastrophe, Rodney Brent signalled his secretary that it was time for coffee. The conversation shifted to interest rates, inflation, baseball, the weather—and then to the Pleasant Valley Church.

"To get to our own backyard," the lawyer said, "I represent Don Turner's dealerships. This is not talking out of school or disclosing a client's affairs but what's going on at your church, Rod? With Merrill? I could tell Don was worried but I didn't know why until my wife ran into Carol Benson. Seems old Don's got religion in a big way. So big he's overhauled his business. Some good people quit."

"You think that's strange? Another with this bug is Ed Vernon. If you think Turner's in trouble, Vernon's on the ropes. Turning down ads, won't run sports news. It's weird. And that fellow, Wes McLain, at the trucking terminal. He's in trouble, too. Same reason."

"You go to the church, Rod. What's Merrill doing, anyway?"

Brent put down his coffee mug. "He ought to mind his own business, stick to church doings, stay out of people's affairs. He's hurting people and he'll hurt a lot more of them before this blows over."

"I thought a minister was supposed to do good, not harm."

Brent nodded, frowned. "I don't know what to say. I wonder sometimes if he hasn't gone crazy. Live life as Jesus would do. That may be fine in the Bible but it won't work in Rockfort."

2

The overflow crowd on Sunday reached out to the sidewalk. Every spare folding chair had been rounded up and placed on the front lawn. A line had been run from a pulpit microphone to a loudspeaker fastened to the railing along the front steps.

Out-of-state license plates, mostly from Ohio and Illinois, were spotted on several cars, their owners lured to Rockfort by press and broadcast stories of Reverend Merrill's dramatic crusade.

Willard Merrill, late in arriving at the church because of an emergency call to the hospital, paused outside and tried to calm himself. He was excited that his work had commanded attention from all over the mid-West; he was uneasy because it was likely that many in the huge crowd were simply curiosity seekers. Then he went to his chair behind the pulpit.

Marsha Hoyt sang and the congregation joined her in Edward Hopper's hymn.

> Jesus Saviour, pilot me
> Over life's tempestuous sea;
> Unknown waves before me roll,
> Hiding rock and treacherous shoal;
> Chart and compass come from thee;
> Jesus, Saviour, pilot me.

As Merrill waited for the finish of the music, he could not shake the intuitive feeling of impending trouble, of rapidly gathering storms of protest and derision.

He began his theme with the last lines of Matthew 25:40. *Verily I say unto you, inasmuch as ye have done it unto one of the least of these my brethren, ye have done it unto me.*

"What do these words mean? Quite simply, if Jesus were living today, he would be concerned with the poor, the less

90

fortunate. If *we* would do as Jesus would do, we must reach out to our brothers and sisters who are besieged with illness, poverty and misfortune. We *are* our brother's keeper! Here in Rockfort, hundreds live in the distress of Sin City, the deprived section of our town. We must do far more in coming to the assistance of these unfortunate souls. This is the only way to follow Jesus. It is the Christian way.

"The key to following Jesus is love—the most important word in our language. Our love for husband, wife, children, friends, neighbors, strangers in need. Yes, even those who have wronged us! Jesus taught love. It is the essence of His teaching. He gave us love so that we might give love in return! If He loves us, are we not to love Him? And if we love Him are we not to follow Him?"

He emphasized the need for courage in following Jesus, and perseverance once we take the first step in following Him. He quoted 1 Peter 3:13: *And who is he that will harm you, if ye be followers of that which is good?*

The minister concluded by announcing a meeting in the Activities Hall of the Followers of Jesus. As Marsha sang, Merrill studied his regulars—the wonderful love on the faces of the Vernons, the Turners, Wes McLain, Virginia. The bright, eager expressions of newer followers. In a front pew was Ellen Heath, wife of the political science professor at Lincoln College.

Reverend Merrill, for the first time in a week, felt that his program was gathering strength. His Followers of Jesus were not just a few random visitors. They were sincere. They took their pledges seriously. They would stay. In spite of all obstacles, they would stay!

Downstairs, the group's meeting was inspired. On this bright June morning, problems were put aside. Ed Vernon rose and spoke. "It hasn't been easy. It may get worse. But on Sundays I put all that out of my mind. Tomorrow I'll keep it out. And the next day, too. Every day I ask myself, 'Can I do it?' And I say, 'Yes. Jesus did it. I can do it.'"

He repeated the words and as a group they all repeated the affirmation aloud. "Yes, I can do it." "Yes, I can do it," they echoed. "I will follow Jesus." "Yes, I will follow Jesus."

There was a moment of silence. Sara Turner spoke: "Show us the way, Reverend." Merrill led them, on their knees, in prayer.

3

At four that afternoon, while Reverend Merrill was praying alone in his study, there was a knock at the door.

"Will, a Mr. Goodman is here to see you. I said you were busy but he said it would only take a minute or two."

"I'll be right out, Ann."

Instinctively, Merrill knew that the extravagantly dressed man was from out of town.

"I'd like a word with you about Marsha Hoyt," Goodman said. When the minister simply stared at him, Goodman looked about questioningly. "Could we…go somewhere?"

"Yes, of course. Forgive my distraction. Right in here."

They went into the living room and sat down.

"Excuse me for barging in like this but I have to fly back to New York in a couple of hours."

"Something about Miss Hoyt?"

"Yes." Goodman blinked, adjusted his glasses. "I'm with General Broadcasting. We made her a terrific offer. To sing, perform, on a new program we're developing. She's a little undecided, a bit reluctant to leave home and her work with you at the church. Her mother feels she'd be crazy not to sign with us."

"I see."

"Mrs. Hoyt thinks a few words from you might help Marsha make up her mind. The young lady thinks the world of you."

"It's a big decision."

"Terrific chance for her. A chance to be a star."

"This is entirely up to Marsha. What made you think I'd advise her what to do?"

"She could come home every summer for a guest shot in church!" Goodman beamed enthusiastically. "Folks would eat it up!" He edged forward on the sofa, took a white envelope from his pocket. "I have here a little donation."

"The Pleasant Valley Church?"

"The network's only too glad to help out." He laughed. "Make things easier while you look for another soloist."

"You realize, Mr. Goodman, that even for Miss Hoyt the work you propose could include a life exposed to sin. The entertainment world is a world of strong temptations and many, unfortunately, succumb. A great contrast to the life Miss Hoyt now leads, a life devoted to following Jesus."

"Sure, but—"

"Mr. Goodman." Willard Merrill rose from his arm chair. "See if I understand you. You'd like me to persuade Miss Hoyt to accept your offer. If she does, you'll make a contribution to our church?"

"Well, yeah. That's basically it."

"You underestimate Miss Hoyt's intelligence." Merrill led Goodman to the hall. "And the church does not accept funds tied to unwise conditions." He stood quietly, and there was nothing further to be said. Goodman nodded to Ann Merrill, who had been a silent observer, and hurried out.

Ann followed her husband to his study.

"That poor girl. What have you done to her? How can you interfere in other people's lives! How much money was it?"

"I have no idea."

"You've no right to refuse a donation. I help you keep the books and the church could use it. The building fund, the children's fund, the hospital fund. Where does the Bible say it's wrong to accept a gift?"

"This was a bribe."

"And you'll go right on, standing up there telling people how to think, what to do, when to do it, and how. It makes me so mad!"

"Jesus had His problems."

"Oh, I knew you'd say something like that! He also had some common sense. He knew enough not to look a gift horse in the mouth. And He knows enough not to come back here and upset things in the twentieth century!"

4

The first full-color edition of the *Herald,* Rockfort's tabloid newspaper, hit the staff of Vernon's conservative *News* like a bombshell.

Long rumored to be in planning stages, the *Herald's* new look included bigger pictures of unclad women, scandalous headlines and stories. Gossip columns. It seemed to feature everything that was bad in society.

Dana Bell, gloomier than usual, brought a copy to Ed Vernon's office. "They've revamped their layout. They'll pick up circulation we're losing."

"What have we lost?" Ed Vernon asked.

"We're down fifteen thousand copies a day. It's snowballing. In two more weeks we'll be back to where we were ten years ago!"

"We can't let that happen."

"These Christian stories of yours, Ed, are killing us. Readers want dirt, Ed, *dirt!* Sex, scandal, murder, rape, incest, gambling!" Bell paused and slowly pointed a finger at his boss. "Know something, Ed? We dropped advertisers, the ones you said were objectionable. Now, the okay ones are dropping us! We're on a toboggan run. All down hill."

Late in the day, Vernon phoned Willard Merrill.

94

The minister arrived at the newspaper in twenty minutes.

"It's reaching the crisis stage, Will," the publisher said. "And timing for the *Herald's* new look couldn't be worse. They're hurting us."

Reverend Merrill closed the door and sat facing Vernon.

"These reactions are to be expected, Ed. Unfortunately. Evil feeds upon itself. We can't let the forces of lust, greed and fear undermine our program. We knew it would be difficult. They don't understand what we're trying to do. So they're fighting us in the only way they know—with derision, scorn, outright hostility."

"How much worse can it get?"

Merrill shook his head. "We don't know that. Let us pray together, right now." They knelt together beside Vernon's desk. "We are not alone, Ed. The Psalmist tells us, *The Lord of hosts is with us; the God of Jacob is our refuge.* We are struggling— we are Jacob in the midst of his troubles—but God is the Lord of hosts—the great Power that will enable us to follow in the path of Jesus, to do as He would do. Jesus spoke of it as 'the Father in me'. John 14:10: *the Father that dwelleth in me, He doeth the works.*"

"If I could just believe that."

"You can, Ed. Jesus loves you. You have to know that. Believe it. You must do more than hope it is true; you must know it beyond all doubt. Our job is to know the love of Jesus is with us and so we are in the right. If we are right, then sin and evil must be wrong. We must hold to that. We must put our trust in the power of the Holy Spirit."

They continued to kneel in silence. As they prayed, Ed Vernon began to feel a renewal of his determination. He felt strong again. After a few moments, when Reverend Merrill had departed, the publisher left his office. He was half way home when he suddenly pulled over and stopped the car.

The harsh facts had come rushing back again, and would not go away. Lost circulation, cancelled advertising, disgruntled, worried employees. And all the other distress. Bad news from Don Turner and Wes McLain. Was Will Merrill blazing a new frontier or was he heading for disaster? Was it fool-hardy to stubbornly cling to the new program? To hurt the *News* and injure its people?

Ed Vernon simply did not know. He was in torment.

The minister drove directly from the *News* to Don Turner's showroom on the Boulevard.

He found the car dealer alone in his office, totally discouraged, looking as if he hadn't slept in a week.

"Thank you for coming by, Will. It hasn't been easy. We lost two salesmen, and a couple of good mechanics. I wasn't prepared, though, for this morning. Jed Benson quit. I didn't try to persuade him to stay. Jed is light years away from our ideas. But he's a top sales manager. He's joined Ed Cunningham's outfit over on Northside."

"I'm sorry to hear it."

The door opened and in came a middle-aged man, stocky, with short, sandy hair and small, ferrett-like brown eyes. "I saw you come in, Reverend Merrill."

"This is Norm Todd," said Turner. "My treasurer."

"To get right to the point," Todd said, dropping into a chair, "we got a problem." He looked directly at Merrill. "And the problem is you!"

"Norm, I think—" Turner protested.

"Never mind. I'm going to say what I came in here to say. I got a stake in this operation, a big stake. Ten years and some big bucks. And I'm telling you, you can't make like you're God running around Rockfort telling folks to imitate Jesus Christ. Kissing everybody's rear while they slap you in the face. Not in the car racket, you can't. We made our ads look like they're running in the Christian Science Monitor. Result—no showroom traffic."

"Honesty in the long run pays off," Merrill observed.

"Maybe at your church. We're honest, Reverend, but we can't do business your way and *stay* in business. What you did

96

was," he looked at Turner, "you took the guts out of the ads. You ruined trade-in dealing. And service is doing work at cost or a markup so small it won't heat the joint next winter. What's with you guys, anyway?"

"Mr. Todd, the world's in trouble. Everywhere there is lying, cheating, stealing, crime, corruption, drugs, child abuse, drunkenness—these things have reached epidemic proportions. Something must be done. Someone has to take the lead, make a start."

"Not at Turner Motors."

"Business should be done on the basis of fairness, trust, dependability, putting the customer first at all times."

"You think our customers are saints? They're ready to rip you off anytime!"

"Isn't it up to you to set the standards?"

"Look at the chiseling. Bad checks. Phony claims on warranties. Don't tell me the public's so saintly. You preacher guys think you can spit out a few Bible words and everything's fine." He jumped to his feet.

"If the world's in sorry shape morally," Merrill asked, "do we just ignore it, let it go from bad to worse?"

"Look. My job is to keep this business profitable, and I don't like a loud-mouth pulpit shouter messing things up!"

"Norm, there's no need to be insulting," Turner said.

"All right!" Todd yelled. "The hell with it!" He glared at Merrill. "Just lay off, you hear? Stop messing around. Go peddle your gospel down at the Boy Scouts." He slammed the door on his way out.

Merrill, aware that Don Turner was extremely distressed, knelt and prayed aloud for understanding, harmony. After a moment Turner joined him. Together they prayed for guidance and strength to go forward. The minister voiced part of Ephesians 3:14-16. *For this cause I bow my knees unto the Father of our Lord Jesus Christ, Of whom the whole family in heaven and earth is named, That he would grant you, according to the riches of his glory, to be strengthened with might by his Spirit in the inner man.* Slowly, Don Turner began to relax. He felt a new energy, a new determination to carry on. Follow Jesus. Do as He would do.

Without a word, Willard Merrill touched the car dealer's shoulder and left the office. In the parking lot, he was about to enter his car when Todd suddenly appeared.

"Listen, Merrill, I'm warning you. Do what you want in that church of yours but stop messing up our operation."

"Don Turner is acting willingly, on his own."

"He'd never got hooked on this stuff without pressure from you."

"It's a volunteer group. Anyone can withdraw."

"Then Turner's got to get out!"

"That's up to him."

"Right now! Before we're hurt anymore. You got him in. I'm telling you to get him out!"

Merrill started to open the door of his car but Todd blocked him. "Hear me? I don't care how you do it, but get Turner out!"

"I must go now."

"You're a crackpot!"

"Please!"

"Out!"

Merrill tried to go around Todd but the treasurer shoved him back. "You hear me?" Todd again shoved the minister. Merrill lost his balance and fell to the blacktop paving. Todd, his face distorted in rage, stood over Merrill, glowering. He kicked the minister, once, twice, three times. Then he walked away.

The minister picked himself up and brushed the dirt from his suit. He entered his car and headed for home. "Dear Jesus," he sighed wearily. "Can I go on? Is it worth it?"

5

Willard Merrill decided to forget the incident in the parking lot. His left leg was bruised and sore where Todd had kicked him, but he quickly ruled out the idea of pressing charges. Any publicity would boomerang—one more happening in a chain of unfortunate events that had reached alarming proportions. Above all, he would say nothing to Ann.

Early next morning he went to see Wes McLain at the East-West terminal. He found Wes, shirt-sleeves rolled up, buried in a mass of records and shipping forms. McLain pulled a letter from an assortment of papers and handed it to the minister.

It was from the parent company in Chicago.

Dear Wes:

This office has received two phone calls and two letters from union representatives on conditions at the Rockfort Terminal.

They register complaints that you have attempted to alter our standard procedures on in-and-out checking, billing, time sheets and in filing insurance claims.

Our policies have been carefully worked out for maximum efficiency, cost-control and maintenance of interstate schedules. Any deviation from these policies, for whatever reason, is unacceptable to management.

You are hereby instructed to strictly observe company rules and regulations as set forth in our Manual of Operations, an extra copy of which is enclosed.

Cordially,

A.B. Weiant
Supervisor, Operations

"You can see where that leaves me," Wes said unhappily.

"Without endangering your job, we must find a way."

"How?"

Merrill shook his head. "I'm not sure. But we'll find it. Right now they're all against us. As if the way of Jesus were some sort of plague to these people."

Wes McLain said: "They might as well throw rocks at us."

The minister grimly reminded himself of the night before when he had been kicked while on the ground. "It's fear," he said thoughtfully. "They fear any change. They fear for their jobs, their incomes. If only they knew how the teachings of Jesus could improve their lives! We can say whatever we wish inside the church but as soon as we reach beyond, into anything that unsettles them, they fight back. It's only natural. We must expect it to happen."

McLain looked at him questioningly. "Then what do we do? We can't give up because they fight us. We can't let them beat us!"

"We'll find a way," Merrill said.

"I wonder if we can."

Rising from his chair, McLain said: "I have to get these bills to the men. It'll only take a few moments."

"I'll go with you."

They went down to the huge warehouse and walked through it toward one of several checking stations on the loading docks. They were half way across the floor when a large man, well over six feet, with close-trimmed blond hair, came over to them.

"This must be the preacher Rollie was tellin' me about. Whatcha doin' here, man, settin' us up to join your outfit? Well, lemme tell ya somethin'. I help Rollie and we ain't takin' no blame for missing goods. You should mind your own damn business and stay to hell outa here."

"Never mind, Hughes!" Wes McLain cautioned.

"No." Merrill said. "Let him speak." He turned to the big man. "Do you know of the word of Jesus? And what it would mean in your life? How much it would help you?"

"Get outa here with that stuff! Don't louse up things around here!" The man disappeared behind an enormous crate.

"Come on," McLain said.

They delivered the bills and returned to McLain's office. "We don't need to take any more of that," Wes grumbled.

They closed the office door and prayed together, asking Jesus to bring peace to their lives and understanding to their antagonists.

Long after Merrill had left, Wes McLain sat at his desk and worried about his situation. He was alternately fortified by prayer, and alarmed over the drastic events crowding his life. The outright hostility among his associates, the stark demands from headquarters. How was he to cope? He was right. Willard Merrill was right. But could they survive the opposition that was growing like a brush fire?

He fought off his gloom and managed to renew himself with prayer and sheer will power. By the time he reached home, he was slightly more optimistic, hopeful that somehow, by some miracle, he would find the answer to his troubles.

Alice McLain was in the kitchen. Jeff sat at the table, his radio blaring out one of the latest rock songs, a can of soda in his hand.

"Hey, Daddio, how's about that mob you had on the lawn at church Sunday?"

"It was a big crowd."

"Some deal! They pass the hat outside, too?"

Alice McLain said: "That church must be taking in loads of money."

"People are coming from all over."

"The whole thing's crazy," Alice declared. "Is Merrill a psycho or what? They'll lock him up first thing you know!"

"He's on the right track."

"And everyone else is nuts, huh?"

101

"I didn't say that."

"But that's what you mean, Wes. When are you going to get some sense and act like a normal man?"

Jeff snorted. "The Followers of Jesus! They're all nuts!"

"It's easy to ridicule. Jesus was scorned."

Jeff and his mother laughed.

"And they pinned Him to the cross!" Jeff smirked.

"I can't talk with you two," Wes said sadly. "You're beyond all help." He went down to his workshop to shut himself away from their cruel remarks. He tried to pray, only to discover he was too upset to think. His mind was a jumble of fears and doubts that crowded out all reason and judgement.

With tears in his eyes he knelt by his workbench and struggled to bring himself under control.

6

After church on Sunday, Marsha and Virginia drove home in Ginny's car.

"The poor in Rockfort are in the Sin City area," Marsha said almost to herself.

"What?" Virginia asked.

"Willard mentioned it in his sermon. Sin City. Maybe that's our project!"

Virginia thought for a moment, then said: "Maybe a mission. In Sin City. Is anyone doing anything down there now?"

"Not much. City Social Services, the fraternal groups, the other churches. They give out food packages at Thanksgiving and Christmas. And clothing."

"Let's drive down there now," Virginia said impulsively. "We might see something. Even on a Sunday."

It was a ten-minute drive down Main Street. They passed a cluster of run-down two-story red brick apartments that had been thrown up in the 1960's as a low-income housing project. Then came a well-worn ball field with remnants of a small grandstand, and two blocks of sad vacant lots strewn with papers, old tires and beer cans.

Sin City itself, known in the 1920's as East Rockfort, and still boasting a sub-station post office under that name, comprised an area of about two square miles. The most prominent buildings were large red brick structures once occupied by machine tool companies, now long idled, with most of the windows broken.

The people of Sin City—estimated to number about 10,000—lived mostly in two and three-story tenements that once housed factory workers, and in battered frame homes, the majority of them badly in need of paint and repairs. Along some six or eight blocks in what could be called the shopping area, about half the stores were boarded up or simply stood empty, generously decorated with weirdly-colored graffiti.

There were numerous bars in Sin City, ranging from small taverns catering mostly to beer drinkers, to the larger places such as Pete's near the center of the area, and Key West, where, it was rumored, the Sin City crime bosses hung out.

Marsha and Virginia parked the car and looked around.

"I didn't think it would be so run-down," Virginia remarked.

"They don't do much about collecting trash or cleaning the sidewalks."

Ginny pointed to the old factories. "How long have they been shut down?"

"Years, I guess."

"We'd need a decent size place for a mission."

"Most of the empty stores are too small."

Marsha started the car. They drove down to a battered stone bridge over Crane's River and turned around. They stopped across from one of the idle factories. East Rockfort Tool Co. was still legible in a cement strip high on the building. Between two wings of the old plant was a low structure that once housed company offices.

"We'll have to think about plumbing and heat."

Marsha said: "This center building is not connected to the main factory. It's the right size. Should we look into it?"

"Why not?"

On the drive back, the two young women exploded with ideas for their project. "We won't just hand out soup and a few warm sweaters," Marsha said. "With a place big enough, we can have activities every morning for seniors. After school we'll get kids in for extra help with homework, for crafts and just plain fun games. Keep them off the streets for a few hours."

"And Will can preach, in the evenings."

They drove quickly to the rectory to see Willard Merrill. Both were too excited to put off telling him. The more they talked over their plans, the more enthusiastic they became. For Virginia, the idea of a mission devoted to helping the poor and unfortunate seemed to be just what she had been seeking. It gave purpose to her life. And Marsha was ecstatic. This was the most important thing that had ever happened to her. She was glad she had said "No" to Mr. Goodman.

They talked for hours with Reverend Merrill. He agreed to have church attorneys look into the abandoned factory, and if it was unavailable, to explore other locations in Sin City.

"What made you two go down there today?"

Marsha smiled. "Your sermon this morning."

"I'm glad it appealed to someone."

"Don't worry," Virginia said. "Plenty of people got the message, Reverend. I think we'll have lots of help."

"If you're right," Merrill said, "it could really get our program under way."

He paused and looked at them. "We'll have to raise quite a bit of money."

"I've thought of that." Virginia said. "I'll see that we get off the ground."

At dinner that evening, Virginia Carver couldn't contain

her enthusiasm. She elaborated on ideas she and Marsha had discussed until finally Geraldine Carver interrupted.

"It's ridiculous! These people have welfare, Medicare, Medicaid, aid to dependent children and God only knows what. Half of them wouldn't work if you offered them jobs!"

"Deeny, most of them are too old, or they don't have the skills, or they're disabled. You can't just rubber stamp all the people who are not as fortunate as we are."

"You'll spend a lot of your money down there and have very little to show for it. Maybe a tax deduction."

"Wait a minute, Deeny," Jerry Carver said. "It's not so crazy. At the club we get lots of appeals for donations. I've heard of cases that are in real need down there."

Virginia looked at her brother in surprise. He had never spoken this way before.

"What's the Government doing?" his aunt asked.

"You can't leave it to the government," Jerry went on. "People have to do more. I'm glad Ginny has an interest in doing more. An objective. It's more than I have."

Jerry thought about the lovely Marsha and tried to visualize her working among the seedy characters in Sin City. He looked respectfully at his sister. "Go to it, Sis. I admire you for what you're doing."

7

For Rodney Brent, dinner at the Rockfort Country Club was a favorite mid-week escape. He found the quiet, unhurried air of the huge Colonial dining room overlooking the ninth hole soothing, almost therapeutic. Here, his friends seldom mentioned the balance of payments or Third World debts let alone overdue bank loans. With their money gainfully employed, they preferred to talk about their expensive cars, condominiums in Sarasota, golfing in Scotland.

On Thursday, Judy Brent had lazed around the pool all day. She grudgingly agreed to stay on for dinner with her father. After cocktails at the bar, they took a table by the window, just beyond reach of the afternoon sun.

"You started to tell me about the Carvers," Judy said.

"Not about the Carver's. *Virginia* Carver. You weren't listening."

"Sorry. What's little rich girl up to now?"

"She's got Merrill fever, real big. She's leased part of a factory down on Mill Street."

"For God's sake! What for?"

"To promote religion."

"How'd you find out?"

"Our real estate people. When the plant went into receivership, we got the building."

Judy sipped her wine while her father continued: "She had to come to us for the lease. They're going to start a mission. All sorts of activities for the poor."

"Who's 'they'?"

"Reverend Merrill, of course. And Marsha Hoyt."

Judy said derisively, "Miss Songbird!"

Brent shrugged. "Put them down if you wish but they're two very attractive women, and they'll be working in the slums in the House of Jesus."

"What! In the House of—"

"It's sort of ridiculous."

"I don't believe this!"

Brent looked out at the golf course, lush and dark green in the fading sunlight. Two Canada geese stood on the edge of a bunker, calmly surveying the white clubhouse. Rodney Brent thought about Cleveland and the big loan that had turned sour. A right to the jaw. He'd be unable to dodge many more. Another Congressional study had just been released in which it was implied that roughly 50 percent of bank failures were caused in part by criminal misconduct by bank officers. A

House Government Operations subcommittee had criticized Federal banking regulators for—Brent remembered the exact words—"not curbing what it termed a rising tide of insider abuse of the nation's financial institutions."

"How much money is Virginia putting up?" Judy inquired.

"It won't put a dent in her holdings."

"What's she worth, anyway?"

When he didn't answer, she said: "A hundred million?"

"A third of that."

"That's enough."

"What does it matter," he said wearily.

She looked up at him. "Hey, are you all right, Dad?"

"Of course."

"You seem worried lately."

"Nothing really."

After dinner they chatted with friends at a nearby table and then headed for home. They were entering the driveway when Judy asked: "Are you sure there isn't something bothering you? I can tell when you're down."

"No. Just tired, that's all."

They locked the front door. She started to go to the pantry. "Have a beer?"

Without answering, he went upstairs to his room.

September

1

They worked fourteen hours a day for three weeks—
Marsha Hoyt, Virginia Carver, Willard Merrill and every volunteer they could enlist. There was help from Ed Vernon,
Wes McLain, Don Turner and other businessmen when they
could get away from their jobs. Ellen Heath gave generously
of her time and brought friends who took over painting chores.

The House of Jesus was in the heart of Sin City. On that
first Sunday, when Marsha and Virginia had driven to the area
for a look around, and on subsequent trips, they had been
too excited about their project to really see Sin City.

They hadn't looked closely at Mill Street, otherwise known
as Sex Street. Here, behind the battered and seemingly closed
doors of small shops that had once sold shoes, hardware,
baked goods, appliances, flowers and meats, there were now
after-hours "clubs," gambling dens and nude shows. What had
been a news stand offering cigarettes, magazines and a few
stationery items on the corner of Mill and First Street was a
smoke shop blatantly selling drugs.

In an old brown-shingle home a block from the mission,
prostitutes openly plied their trade. Pornographic movies and
peep shows attracted a steady flow of customers to a former
clothing store. From the traffic in and out of Sin City it was
clear that many of the area's customers came from better
sections of Rockfort and from various cities and towns around
the state. Sin City had a reputation. Buy what you want. Go
the limit. Your chance of being arrested was minimal. And
if you were apprehended by some over-eager officer, you paid
a small fine and walked away.

What was Sin City really like? If the mission was going to be there, Willard Merrill had to know. He decided to find out. Into this sea of degradation he arrived in late afternoon on a Friday, an hour before the official, much publicized opening of the House of Jesus.

Clad in well-worn jeans, a light gray windbreaker, sneakers, and wearing dark-tinted sunglasses, Merrill might have passed for someone from an adjoining neighborhood or as a resident of Sin City itself.

He had told no one of his plans. He wanted to explore Sin City himself. How bad were conditions? What priorities were to be established? Where might the strongest opposition be encountered?

Beginning at the corner of First Street, with the new mission six blocks to the east, he walked slowly down Mill Street. He entered Pete's bar, where he went to a pay phone and pretended to make a call while he looked around. Suddenly there was a harsh blast of rock music and a young blond girl, nude from the waist up, was spotlighted on a high ledge behind the bar. The patrons responded with wild yells, whistling and cat-calls. The girl smiled and began to go through furious gyrations in tune with the music. She started to disrobe further. Merrill hung up the receiver and quietly made his exit.

At his next stop, he paid an admission charge and found himself in a dark room where a small movie screen was graphically portraying the sexual antics of two nude figures. Merrill left without attracting attention. The audience was entranced with the film. The attendant seemed to be barely conscious.

Merrill entered a stationery store. He watched six underage young people buy liquor from a supply stashed under the counter. Two young girls made additional purchases— small white packets, obviously containing drugs.

He stopped in front of the Key West Bar & Grill. It appeared to be the largest establishment on the street. He went past the long, crowded bar to the telephone booth. His attention was attracted to the number of men entering and leaving a back room. Curious, he followed the traffic. Inside he found himself in a cavernous room. On one side was a long blackboard with horse race results. There were teller booths, as in a bank. Over the loudspeaker results were being announced. The remainder of the room was taken up with 20 or 30 tables at which men played with cards and dice, money and chips piled high in front of them.

Shaken by what he had seen, Willard Merrill made his way along Mill Street. He was approached by a flashily dressed young girl with a chorus-line makeup and long braids of black hair. "Got the time, buddy?" The minister hurried past her, aware of her inviting eyes.

A key idea behind the House of Jesus was to campaign against illicit sex and to fight gambling, drugs, alcohol.

Merrill shook his head. It was a tall order.

The office building at the old plant had been cleaned and painted. Partitions had been shifted to make a large meeting room and provide smaller rooms for special programs. The plumbing and heating had been modernized. There were folding chairs, tables, a piano, a record-player—all donated. In the rear were two long, narrow areas to be used as dormitories.

The opening ceremonies began promptly at seven o'clock. At the last minute, the mayor of Rockfort, who had been scheduled to make the opening address, sent his apologies; he'd be unable to attend because of an emergency budget meeting.

Willard Merrill, changed into a business suit, stood before a crowd of about two hundred that filled the hall. There were young and old, more women than men. Most were shabbily dressed. All had vacant expressions tinged here and there with traces of expectancy.

Merrill welcomed them to the House of Jesus, told why the mission was being started, described programs to be offered, stressed that help would be given to all who sought it. There would be no charge for anything; the staff was on a volunteer basis.

He introduced and praised Marsha Hoyt and Virginia Carver, the mission's directors. Then Marsha sang Psalm 23:3,5-6. *He restoreth my soul: He leadeth me in the paths of righteousness for His name's sake* in her own musical arrangement. During her solo, two men drifted in and stood at the rear of the packed room.

They were familiar figures in Sin City. Mort Freel was the younger. He was stout, about five nine, with thinning brown hair and brown eyes. He wore a plaid sports jacket, gray slacks and was tie-less. His companion was Lennie Grob, a slender man with deep lines in a craggy face and a shock of unruly gray hair. He, too, was casually dressed in soft colors.

Willard Merrill's sermon began with Hebrews 2:18. *For in that he himself hath suffered being tempted, he is able to succour them that are tempted.*

"He is able to help us! Why, then, are we buried in sin? Why do we fall victims of drugs, alcohol? And of gambling? Why do we see, right here on Mill Street, young women soliciting those who will pay for their services? Why, only an hour ago, did I see young people, teenagers probably in high school, buying drugs and whiskey?"

Eyes flashing, his clear-cut features set determinedly, Merrill's voice rose in indignation. "If it were not available a few doors from this mission, people would not come to Sin City for illegal sex. If youngsters, who should be in healthy activities, could not buy heroin, cocaine, gin, vodka, rum and whiskey, they'd find healthy and constructive things to do with their time and money. Gambling—whether it be on horses, with cards or dice—requires owners, operators. Evil, immoral people greedily stuffing their pockets with ill-gotten cash

111

taken from the misery of others. Sin requires providers! Pitchmen who hawk their wares and promote their wretched products blatantly, openly, without regard for law and decency!

"Our New House of Jesus," he continued, "is a haven for those who want something better in their lives. Those who are trying to escape from sin. The hungry and homeless. The poor, the sick, the disabled, the elderly, the aimless young will find this new mission a refuge. Understanding and comfort will be offered here every day, twenty-four hours a day."

As he spoke, Grob and Freel shuffled uneasily, whispering to one another. When Merrill prepared to close his remarks, the two men eased out the door. The audience was invited to have coffee or soup, and sandwiches. Most of them formed a line before a long table set up near the kitchen.

Willard, Virginia and Marsha sighed in relief. The opening was behind them. On their faces were smiles of satisfaction. They had made a good start. And a great challenge lay ahead!

Virginia and Marsha were the happiest they had ever been. Merrill glowed. It was so rewarding. To help others. Especially to help those who had been overlooked in life.

2

In a dingy, smoke-filled room above the Key West Bar and Grill, Mort Freel closed the door and sat at a table facing Lennie Grob.

"I don't care how we do it, the joint's gotta be shut down."

Grob blinked. "That guy's trouble."

"Our take in this town is big. No bugs up to now. How'd this jerk get the idea to come down here, anyway?"

"I heard he's stirrin' up people in his church."

"Then let him keep his act up there."

"That Carver dame put up a bundle for the old building and fixed it up."

"And the singer's in with her?"

"Yeah."

"Then we got more than just his holiness."

"A lot more. Word is a car dealer and Vernon, who owns the *News,* is in the deal."

Mort Freel sat back in his chair and blew a cloud of smoke up at the small lamp over the table. "It took us eight years to get control. First, the guys at City Hall, then the boys at the State Capitol. They're with us, they know what's good for them. Now we got these angels of mercy buttin' in. The mission's got to go!"

"Shall I call the boys?"

"Yeah, let's get movin'."

3

With Ed Vernon in the conference room were Dana Bell, managing editor; Joel Watkins, advertising director; Ev Marno, treasurer; and Brad Steever, circulation manager. Their faces reflected the gloomy tone of the hastily called meeting. There were the usual mugs of coffee, yellow pads, sharpened pencils.

Dana Bell leaned forward. "For weeks we haven't touched a story about violence, sex crimes, drugs, racing or anything that smacks of gambling."

When the others were silent, Bell went on. "If wire stories are hairy, we ignore them. Like that one last week about the Chicago woman who threw her kid out the window. What do *we* do? Stuff about a dame who does volunteer work at the hospital. Church news. A family of eight that goes to church together. Today's Bible story."

Brad Steever cut in, "What Dana says is killing our circulation. Dealers' returns are getting worse every day.

And home deliveries are off."

"What have we lost, Brad?" the treasurer asked.

Steever looked at his notes. "About 18,000 to 20,000 copies. But we lag a couple of weeks. It's worse now."

Ed Vernon, who had listened patiently, nodded to Joel Watkins of advertising. Watkins was well prepared. He consulted a small pocket notebook. "We cancelled around thirty thousand bucks—these are monthly figures—as contracts came up. But what murders us is the drop with our best clients." He went back to his little book. "Bentley's Hardware. The Bargain Corner. Murphy's. Several others. They reduced their schedules, like they're waiting for us to come out of the fog."

"What's the month look like?" Steever asked.

"Awful," Watkins moaned. "Total ad revenue, not counting classified and national, will be down at least forty thousand."

"National will hold up," Ed Vernon said.

"Are you kidding?" Watkins continued. "Wait 'til the agencies get the word. We'll be giving rebates based on lower circulation."

Ed Vernon sighed. "It's not a good picture."

Two of the men laughed bitterly.

Ev Marno, the treasurer, spoke up. "We're running, in gross dollars, about sixty thousand a month under last year. It can't go on. Our reserves were mostly used up when we put in the new presses."

There was a long silence. The four key men on the *Rockfort Daily News* looked at Ed Vernon. He was the boss. He was the big shareholder. He called the shots. The only way to unseat Ed Vernon would be by voting a change. But how can you unseat a man who owns most of the voting stock?

"Our new policies are very unpopular," Vernon admitted.

"They're worse than that, Ed," Watkins said. "They're a disaster!"

Dana Bell chimed in. "It's even worse with the new look at the *Herald*. Sex, scandal, violence, gossip. They're up at least twenty thousand copies a day."

There was nothing Ed Vernon could say. He couldn't dispute the figures. He needed time to think and to work out the problem on his own terms. He needed time to pray. In his heart he knew he would never go back to the old way of doing business. And yet he couldn't just sit by and watch the *News* go under.

The decision was made to lay off thirty employees.

4

Sitting at Don Turner's desk was Fred Schaeffer. A confident man with light blond hair, he had risen meteorically from district parts manager in northern New England to regional sales manager in charge of six Midwestern states.

"What's wrong, Don?"

Turner was slow in answering. "We've made some policy changes. Drastic at first, better in the long run."

"You've come to a dead stop."

"We're adjusting. It'll take time."

"You've got the biggest inventory, based on average volume, of any dealer in my territory. The last ten days you haven't sold enough new cars to fill my driveway."

"I know it's been off."

"Every other dealer is up over last year. You're down. And Jed has left. He was a good man, Don. How come?"

"Better offer."

"Nonsense! He left because you're into some religious thing. I know the story. Two of your best salesmen quit, too. The boys around the state tell me it's some kind of a Jesus crusade. What's happened to you, Don?"

Don Turner had known all along that this was bound to happen. And yet Merrill was right. In truth he, Turner, was right. But was it enough to be right? Could you succeed by being right? Doing business honestly, decently, fairly?

"We're using honest sales policies," said Turner emphatically.

Schaeffer exploded. "I can't believe I'm hearing this! From you? After ten years?"

"In the end you'll see we're right."

"I should live that long! Listen, Don, your franchise is up for renewal this fall. You're going to need a turnaround in sales. Do you understand?"

Don Turner looked away. From his glass partitioned office he could survey the entire showroom, the business he had worked so hard to build. As if on cue, Willard Merrill came in on his daily visit. Turner almost wished the minister had chosen another time. The introduction was forced, awkward.

Fred Schaeffer resumed his seat and lit a cigarette. "So this is our evangelist friend. Bought a new car lately, Reverend?"

"No."

"I'll bet not! And neither has anyone else around this store." He smiled scornfully. "Have you had much experience in the car business, Reverend? Do you understand the psychology of selling cars? I guess not, judging from what's happening around here."

Willard Merrill said: "Quite a few intelligent folks in Rockfort think we're right. You must admit there's room for improvement in morals, in relationships, in the way we do business."

"Maybe," Schaeffer replied. "But the good Lord wouldn't want us to go broke, would he?"

"Of course not."

"Right! I trust you'll change your mind in a hurry, Reverend. I don't know how many other outfits you've influenced but the best thing you can do is keep your Bible teachings in church."

Schaeffer rose abruptly, went to the door. "Renewal time is December."

116

They watched him stride across the showroom and disappear. For a moment neither Willard Merrill nor Don Turner spoke. Their faces reflected the blunt warning.

Merrill knelt and Turner followed. The minister said, "In Acts 18:9-10, Jesus told us: *Be not afraid, but speak, and hold not thy peace: For I am with thee and no man can set on thee to hurt thee...*"

They prayed together to Jesus for help, guidance, strength.

"There has to be a way," Merrill insisted, "a course of action that will not mean total disruption in your business, Don. And a way for us to continue with our program at the same time. We've got to find that way."

"How can the way of Jesus encounter such terrible opposition?" Turner asked. "Are people so blinded by self-interest and greed they can't see the light?"

"They will come around," Merrill said quietly. "I know it. We can't give up now. The last thing I want, Don, is to see your business suffer. Let us pray every moment that it will not come to that. We can't give up now. The new mission is under way. It will give us a lift. People will respect us for what we're trying to do."

"I never thought it would be this bad."

"Hold on. Pray. The Holy Spirit will lead us. I'll come by tomorrow as usual."

The minister went on his way. Throughout the day and on the drive home, Don Turner could not shake his fears. He could not forget Fred Schaeffer's words.

"Renewal time is December."

5

The visitor from union headquarters in Chicago meant trouble. Wes McLain had been talking with him for twenty minutes. He was Mel Prosser, a short, dark, well-dressed young man with large gold-rimmed glasses. Prosser might have passed for a stockbroker or a lawyer. Until he opened his mouth. Then he was a street-smart, high-school dropout.

"Look at these reports," Prosser said. "Double-check each shipment! Count each piece! A guy don't make his schedules doin' that. They get paid for time. Rollie Makin figures from Des Moines to Pittsburgh a driver can lose twenty to forty bucks horsin' around this way. Ten minutes here, twenty someplace else. It adds up."

"I intend to run a straight operation here."

"Look, McLain. My boss says what you're doin's gotta stop."

"And we go right on being dishonest?"

"What's it to you? You sit on your butt and draw your pay. Forget what's happening on the road. They breakdown, they jack-knife, they go to sleep at the wheel." He dropped his cigarette on the floor and stepped on it. "They move the merchandise, don't they?"

"Mr. Prosser," Wes said firmly. "Things will never get better in this industry until we wipe out stealing. I'm trying to make a start."

"Oh, yeah! Well, lissen, buddy! Take your goody-goody junk and shove it. We got rules. Rules agreed between the union and operators. All operators. Don't try to louse things up."

"The rules should be changed."

Suddenly Prosser's face swelled, flushed in rage. He banged his right hand down on McLain's desk, scattering a holder filled with yellow pencils and sending papers flying.

"Don't tell me about rules. You got nothin' to do with rules!" he stormed. "We make the rules! Your job is to stick to them."

"You're telling me what my job is?"

"Damn right I am! And I'm tellin' you to lay off. Wise up. Get off our backs. Or we call a job action. How'd you

118

like a nice strike here? Let Chicago hear about *that* and you'll be walkin' the street in twenty minutes. When Makin and Stacy called me about this Jesus junk I told them they was out of their minds. Now I see what they're talkin' about. Wait 'til I tell the big boys about what's goin' on." He rose. "You got twenty-four hours to get off whatever you're smoking. Noon tomorrow. Or I blow the whistle on you."

Wes McLain felt numb. Alone, he stared into space, thankful that it was lunch hour and things were quiet. At last he rose, went to the window and looked down at the long lines of trailers at their loading bays. Everything at a standstill between now and one o'clock. In ten minutes the loaders and checkers would appear, taking up where they'd left off, moving back and forth on their routines, joking, sweating, swearing, waiting for their coffee break. Wes McLain tried to work. It was impossible.

He paced his small office. Several times he made sure the door was locked and knelt in prayer, asking Jesus for answers to his overwhelming troubles. He pictured his mother, sitting by a battered wood stove in a shack in Georgia, her Bible on her knees, trying to comfort him. Once again he heard her voice in slow, measured tones. "Let not your heart be troubled, son, neither let it be afraid."

He saw her gentle smile, felt her comforting hand, saw himself kneeling beside her on the rough wooden floor. "Mother, I try. I try not to be afraid. I try! They don't understand! I know it says in John 16:33 *In the world ye shall have tribulation: but be of good cheer; I have overcome the world."* With tears in his eyes, he cried out: "Can I do this, Mother? Can I overcome?"

Later, tired and discouraged, he went down to his car to go home.

The windshield had been smashed.

119

After their successful opening, Marsha Hoyt and Virginia Carver were swamped. They worked long hours. But it was not enough to take care of the flood of people attracted to the House of Jesus.

It was clear that four departments were needed: a thrift shop for the sale of clothing and household items; a placement desk for part-time jobs; activities for seniors; and a program for young people. Plus food services and housekeeping chores.

One by one, volunteers were recruited. Ellen Heath took responsibility for youngsters, age 10 to 18. Janet Lauder, already chairlady of activities at the church, agreed to organize the seniors' program; Helen Saco, who had run a beauty salon in Sin City, was put in charge of the thrift shop, and Kate Bron, a personnel director recently retired from the hospital, was willing to run job placement. It was a good, dedicated group.

Willard Merrill came to their first meeting and spoke on the purpose of the mission. "There is so much to be done. So many individuals who can use our help. If we move just a small step ahead each day, think what we can accomplish here at the House of Jesus! Fighting sin, poverty, sickness, unhappiness, lawlessness. Making better lives for others—and ourselves." There was a vigorous round of applause. "Let's make the House of Jesus a house that never stops growing!" He concluded with hearty praise for the volunteers.

When it was found that first-floor space previously allocated for dormitories was needed for other purposes, Virginia called in a contractor to renovate the upper floor to provide two dorms.

Virginia and Marsha were at the front door, waiting for the contractor to confirm a starting date, when they saw a familiar car drive up. Grace Hoyt and Geraldine Carver got out and stood on the sidewalk, looking up at the battered old red-brick building.

Moving determinedly, the two women swept in past the girls to the main hall where 40 or 50 persons were reading, playing checkers, talking or dozing in their chairs.

"Welcome to our mission," said Marsha cordially. "What a nice surprise to see you both here."

There was an awkward silence. Then Grace Hoyt spoke in a loud voice. "We had to see with our own eyes. The *News,* the radio stations—and then television the other night—had stories on you." She waved an arm at the ceiling. "How do you propose to heat this barn?" A dozen heads looked up in surprise.

"There's a brand new furnace," Virginia answered.

"It seems to me, Ginny, there might be better places to spend your money," Geraldine Carver said. "Your father gave generously to the Shriners and the Red Cross, and he left a small fortune to Lehigh, his college, but I doubt if he ever intended his money to be wasted on a lot of down-and-outers who don't work and never will."

"Deeny, look around," Virginia said quietly. "These people are old, many of them. Some are disabled. They're poor because of circumstances beyond their control. We've only been open a week and they love the mission. Come, we'll show you around."

The girls led the way to other rooms. "We have so much going on," Marsha said.

"More than you can handle, I'd say," Grace Hoyt observed.

"No," Virginia answered. "We're getting new volunteers to help every day. It's very exciting."

Geraldine Carver asked: "Are all these people waiting for a handout?"

Marsha smiled. "Not at all. Many of them are discouraged, some are desperate. When you help them, even in a small way, their faces light up. They're so grateful."

They went into the kitchen area. The two older women haughtily inspected the range, the sink, shelves with dishes.

"How in the world do you feed this crowd?" Grace Hoyt asked.

"It's easy when you have help. One full-time person prepares meals. The volunteers clean up. You see, Mom, when these people appreciate every little thing you do for them, it's no longer work. It's a joy. Just to see them react that way makes you understand what Jesus meant when he said: *Blessed are the poor in spirit: for theirs is the kingdom of heaven.*"

"And they'll always be with us!" Grace Hoyt declared. Then she added: "The Lord helps those who help themselves."

"But what about those who can't help themselves?" replied Virginia.

"We come here to the mission every day and we're uplifted," Marsha added. "A look on an old lady's face that is different from when we first saw her. A youngster smiling after being sad, and down. When you see these changes, and what this place means to people, it's thrilling!"

"Well—" Grace Hoyt began.

"Wouldn't you like to see the upstairs? We'll have new dorms ready in a few weeks. Then more room will be available down here."

Mrs. Hoyt stiffened. "I think not." She surveyed the ceiling. "I've seen quite enough, thank you."

"Some other time, Ginny," Geraldine Carver said with a trace of warmth. The two women, as though acting on cue, started for the front door.

They turned in the hall. Grace Hoyt glared at her daughter. "You're here in this...slum, when you could be in New York. You'll regret not accepting Goodman's offer! You'll regret it to your dying day!"

They left silently, as abruptly as they had arrived.

7

Jerry Carver sat at the card table in the City Club with Andy Harkness, his long-time friend, Scotch in front of them, cards in hand. It was their daily game, following lunch.

"What's all this about Virginia?" Andy asked. "A settlement house in Sin City? Someone saw her waxing floors."

"She's working with Marsha Hoyt. The Church is behind it. Ginny put up a few bucks to help them get started."

"I heard it was a bundle."

Jerry smiled. "I sort of admire them for what they're doing. Trying to help people."

"That's a tough part of town for those girls to be in. You've any idea of what goes on in Sin City?"

"Sure."

"It's bad."

"I'm not worried."

"Jerry, those girls could get killed down there."

8

The senior vice president in charge of loans at County Trust Company was Carter Keene, a big, florid man who wore coarse tweed suits that made him appear even heavier than his flabby 220 pounds.

"Rodney," he said softly. "The delinquent-loan list has grown steadily. We now have 27 past-due loans of more than two hundred thousand each."

Rod Brent stared at the huge man, then glanced at a pad on his desk and pretended to be adding figures. It was old news. If truth were known, the bank's non-performing loans ran above 27. But it wasn't the number; it was the dollar amount that counted. Brent's old friend in Cleveland, owing twelve million dollars and unable to pay even the interest, was the big bad boy. Only Brent knew how bad. So far the banker had not told his associates. Two days ago, the Federal Deposit Insurance Corporation had called, seeking information that Brent had promised to supply without delay. He had done nothing about it.

"Yes, Carter. Give me a few hours. We have to come up with some answers. The FDIC has been on the phone."

Carter Keene paled slightly. "I didn't know that."

When Keene had left, Rod Brent closed his eyes and massaged his forehead with his three middle fingers. If only he could get a night's sleep without pills. The stuff left him so groggy the next day it was all he could do to stay awake in mid-afternoon.

He had given Keene part of the bad news. Within a few minutes the entire office would know about the FDIC. What they didn't know—the worst part—was that right now a man from the office of The Comptroller of the Currency in Washington was on his way to Rockfort.

9

Rockfort's Committee of Fifty, organized in the '60's by Rodney Brent, was comprised of the city's richest, most influential business and professional leaders. They met monthly for luncheon at the Madison Hotel. They were top company executives, bankers, retailers, attorneys, insurance and real estate men. They led all charity drives, donated liberally to hospitals and fraternal organizations, and instructed state senators on how to vote.

Rodney Brent was happy to escape from his office and further contact with Carter Keene. He stood before the Fifty after dessert and coffee were served and read routine announcements. Then he turned the meeting over to an accountant who gave a brief run-down of Rockfort business conditions—plant openings and closings, retail sales figures, employment statistics, tax adjustments.

"On employment," the accountant said, looking up from his notes, "The *News* laid off thirty people. Most of you know that."

There was an immediate reaction. An attorney with a prominent law firm spoke up. "No excuse for it, either. Everyone in this city knows what's been going on at one of our finest churches. A crusade. If we don't watch out, we'll be burning witches in Rockfort."

"Hey, hey!" The chorus came from a table near the podium.

The head of a food-processing plant rapped on his water glass. "I had lunch with Don Turner yesterday. He's in danger of losing his GM franchise."

"Why?" someone shouted.

"Jesus. The minister's got him on a Bible kick. Love thy neighbor. Steal from me. Rape my wife. I still love you."

When the laughs subsided, an insurance man spoke up. "Did you hear that East-West may get a walkout? The men have been accused of stealing!"

Rodney Brent was back at the podium. He waited until the chatter stopped. "I know a little about this. I attend the Pleasant Valley Church." He paused and then added, pontifically, "I help support it."

There was a round of scattered applause and a few cheers.

"Seems Reverend Merrill is off on a holier-than-thou campaign. He's got a mandate from a small crowd of followers who are giving their time, spending their money and causing all sorts of trouble."

"Then stop him!" a voice from the rear advised.

"It's not that simple," Brent continued. "He's done nothing illegal—yet. His people have leased an old building on Mill Street and started a mission."

A real estate broker was on his feet. "I have two clients who own property down there. They don't like all this disturbance.

They want Sin City left alone."

"This guy Merrill," the attorney announced, "is the reason Ed Vernon and Don Turner are in trouble."

"If he wants to start a mission, why doesn't he go to Africa? They need him over there."

"Is this the thing the Carver girl's mixed up in?"

"Yes! Spends every day there." Brent was enjoying his role of informer. "She and Marsha Hoyt, the church soloist."

Another attorney spoke up. Dressed in a three-piece black suit he oozed respectability. As a sideline he owned a prosperous small loan business in Sin City. "Look. This Merrill is responsible not only for Vernon and Turner being in trouble but McLain, too. And he's causing real trouble in Sin City. How long are we going to let this go on?"

"What can you do?" asked Brent.

"I'll tell you what we can do. We can run Merrill out of town. Run him out of town!"

10

History was made at the Pleasant Valley Church on a bright, hot Sunday in late summer. Responding to requests from all over the state, the service was broadcast on Rockfort's leading radio station. Standing before a microphone and another overflow crowd, inside and outside the church, the minister spoke of the House of Jesus, told of its progress and its volunteers. Then he linked the neighborhood known as Sin City directly to the first three verses of Psalm 37: 1-3. *Fret not thyself because of evil-doers, neither be thou envious against the workers of iniquity.*

For they shall soon be cut down like the grass, and wither as the green herb.

Trust in the Lord, and do good; so shalt thou dwell in the land, and verily thou shalt be fed.

"Who are the evil-doers the psalmist mentions? They are the merchants of Sin City, the purveyors of drugs, prostitution, gambling, illegal alcohol. They are the peddlers of drugs who drove a broken-hearted woman from King Street to my office yesterday. She begged me to help her son who is trapped by the drug habit. They are the sellers of alcohol who cater to our youngsters. One in particular—a high-school sophomore whose father telephoned me Friday night in desperation. How long can we allow these workers of iniquity to be among us? Should they not be cut down like the grass? Wither as the green herb? They can be overcome if we trust in the Lord, and do good. *We* shall dwell in *our* land, and be fed by His grace and love and inspiration!

"What would Jesus do about this sinful condition in Rockfort? Jesus was a man of action. He would take action. And we will take action! We will move against the forces of evil and sin! Today! Together! We will follow Jesus!"

Merrill called for a campaign to close after-hours clubs, gambling establishments, houses of prostitution, dealers in drugs and those who sell liquor to minors. He went to the heart of the matter and urged a new mayor for Rockfort. He asked for suggestions, a man who would clean up Sin City, a man willing to pick up his cross and follow Jesus. Then the minister sat down.

The congregation was stunned into silence. Many looked at one another and whispered back and forth. A few reacted emotionally, tears in their eyes.

Marsha Hoyt sang her own musical arrangement of the hymn, *Lord Jesus, Think On Me* by Ernest W. Shurtleff.

Lord Jesus, think on me,
And purge away my sin;
From earthborn passions set me free,
And make me pure within.

Lord Jesus, think on me,
Amid the battle's strife;
In all my pain and misery
Be thou my health and life.

The congregation sat quietly until the last note. At the door, Merrill was showered with praise as small groups formed to discuss the provocative sermon.

Jerry Carver waited patiently. When Willard Merrill said the last "thank you" and headed for the customary group meeting, Jerry grasped his hand. "A fine sermon, Reverend. A good idea." A surprised Merrill looked at him questioningly, smiled and went downstairs.

Waiting for Merrill in the Activities Hall were Roger and Ellen Heath. The Lincoln College professor of political science had wondered, during the sermon, if some divine coincidence might have lured him to church on this particular Sunday. His wife had lost no time. No sooner were they in the hall when she had whispered, "It's what you've wanted, Roger, what we've talked about. Doing something. Not just lecturing to classes on the passing parade. But getting *into* the parade. Participating."

"What do you mean?"

"It was no accident. Your coming to church with me today. I felt it when we both kneeled in prayer. I felt that some power was guiding us, leading us."

"I felt it, too," Roger Heath said. "I wanted to go on praying. It was that strong. But the congregation sat back in the pews again."

"Well?"

"Yes, if they want me, I'll run for Mayor."

Ellen smiled broadly and her eyes filled with tears of joy.

It was the largest meeting of the Followers of Jesus so far. There were accounts of problems at home, and suggestions for dealing with them. Merrill, fully aware of the acute troubles of Vernon, McLain and Turner, knew that others, with only their families to be concerned about, were nevertheless facing

128

serious stress as they attempted to follow Jesus in their everyday lives.

"I have my doubts, too," Merrill admitted to the group. "Am I doing right? I ask myself that question a hundred times a day. Can each one of us live a life as Jesus would live it? Or is that asking the impossible? Are we being impractical? Then I look at the world outside, with its unbelievable sorrow, immorality, crime and corruption and I say to you that we *can* do it! We'll prove that it is possible! We will do it through our own convictions of what is right, and with the leadership of the Holy Spirit. Let us kneel and pray."

The minister prayed for help and guidance in the program and at the House of Jesus. Then he read from John 13:34-35. *A new commandment I give unto you, that ye love one another; as I have loved you, that ye also love one another. By this shall all men know that ye are my disciples, if ye have love one to another.*

11

That evening, Ann Merrill was even more upset than usual. "Aren't you going too far, Will, getting into politics, trying to pick a new mayor of Rockfort?"

"Not if you look at the reasons. There are terrible problems in this city. We need help at the top. We need a city government that will crack down on evil and vice and crime."

Ann shook her head, and her lips tightened.

"You seem like another person, a stranger."

"Don't say that."

"I can't help it. That's the way I feel."

He went to her and put his arms around her.

"We'll get through this. Look at all the calls we had from people who heard us on the radio today. People everywhere are beginning to understand."

"Will, how can you say that?" She pulled away from him. "They're just curious. Don't you see? There's nothing but trouble from this stubbornness of yours!"

"Do you really think that?"

"Yes, I do. And I've never been so miserable in my life."

He watched her turn and quickly go to the kitchen.

In his study, he closed the door and prayed. He and Ann were growing apart. It had never been like this before.

Willard Merrill prayed to Jesus to save his marriage.

Help me in this terrible time. Let your peace and understanding enfold my home, quell the despair in my marriage. Dear Jesus, renew and restore love as it has been in our lives. Help us to again know your love and compassion. I trust in you. I believe in you.

12

Ed Vernon was at the breaking point. Earlier in the day, he and his department heads had taken the inevitable step: they had laid off 35 more employees. Vernon clenched his fists and paced the floor. Something had to be done. He could not wreck the paper entirely. Follow Jesus? Yes! But how far? Ruin the lives of sincere, honest people, many of whom had been with the *News* for years?

There was a knock at the door and Gabe Mendon came in. He was 57 years old, a pressman, a veteran. He stood before Vernon, hands clasped, his thin frame bent slightly, his blue-gray eyes glazed with fear. His shaky voice was barely audible. "Mr. Vernon, I couldn't believe it. Thirty-nine years I have with the *News*. They said something about early retirement but I can't get social security yet."

"I know."

"I have this son at home. He don't improve any. Some mental thing, they say. If I could stay on another five years, to sixty-two, I might—" He stopped, unable to continue; his lips trembled despairingly.

Ed Vernon rose and put his arm around Mendon's scraggy shoulders. "It's not right, Gabe. We must do something. I know what you're going through." Vernon moved slowly away from the man. "I'll talk with Dana. I can't promise you anything. We've had to take drastic action or go under entirely. It's that simple."

"Just five years, Mr. Vernon," Mendon pleaded.

"I'll try."

Gabe Mendon left and Ed Vernon faced the blackest moment of his life. How could he do this to innocent people? Was any cause, *any program at all,* worth this much human suffering? Couldn't they follow Jesus and still not hurt others? Why should Gabe Mendon suffer? What would Jesus do? Would he bring pain to sixty-five employees at the *Rockfort News?* True, some of the discharged workers almost welcomed early retirement. They were mostly men and women in their early sixties. They had saved something. They had grown sons and daughters. Many would share homes with relatives until they began to collect social security. But there were other Gabe Mendons—pressmen, typesetters, make-up men, re-porters, ad salespeople, delivery truck operators. They were bitter and resentful. Ed Vernon knew they blamed him. They asked, "Why does Vernon have to get mixed up in this crack-pot minister's insanity?"

13

While dinner grew cold, Ed Vernon's wife and daughter tried to comfort him.

"I can't go on," Vernon said. "I hate what we're doing to people. It's much worse than I ever imagined. And all my fault.

131

There must be a way I can stay with Will Merrill's plan and still not cause such misery."

"What can you do, Dad?"

"I wish I knew."

"Give it up?"

Vernon shook his head. "I feel trapped."

"Are you thinking of going back—to the way things were?" Barbara asked.

"Don't you see what that would do? The mission is under way. Our program has been broadcast all over the mid-west. The *News* is in the spotlight. A newspaper is a very public thing. Everyone watches what we do. Much more so than in a car dealership or a business like trucking. We're so visible." He paced the floor and continued, bitterly. "If we tried to hire back the employees and change the paper back to what it was, they'd laugh at us. 'Vernon threw in the towel.' 'Vernon quit.' 'Vernon gave up.' 'The fire was too hot for Vernon.' How can we go back now?"

"Merrill would understand," Barbara said.

"Sure he would," Ed Vernon agreed. "He's always left it up to us. No pressure. But it's too late. I'm not even sure they'd go back to buying the paper and picking up their ad schedules. People like to kick you when you're down."

"That doesn't sound like you, Ed."

"Dad, it'll work out. Something will happen. You'll worry yourself sick if you don't stop!"

Ed Vernon put his arms around his daughter, and Barbara rushed to embrace them both.

"Thank God for you two," Vernon said.

After a moment, Barbara said, "Let's call Will."

The minister insisted on coming over at once.

"We'll find a way," Reverend Merrill said. "We must! The *News* is part of us. It cannot fail. our program will not fail. Working together, we will overcome!"

132

He saw the doubt and worry on their faces.

"Come, let us join together in prayer. Let us indeed *Be still and know that He is God.* In this time of deep trouble, we turn to Him. Our faith is in Him. We believe in His love and know that rightness must prevail in our lives."

"Join with me now, repeat after me these words from Psalm 6:8-10: *Depart from me, all ye workers of iniquity; for the Lord hath heard the voice of my weeping. The Lord hath heard my supplication; the Lord will receive my prayer. Let all my enemies be ashamed and sore vexed: let them return and be ashamed suddenly."*

By the time Merrill left, the Vernons felt better. But soon their doubts and fears returned.

"Perhaps we should go back to the way things were, for now, anyway," Barbara said tearfully. "I just don't know!"

"What will happen to us, Dad?" Hildy wondered.

"We must pray for help, constantly."

"If we just lived our lives, went to church on Sundays, and helped the poor as much as possible, wouldn't that be enough?" Barbara asked. "We can't go on like this!"

Throughout the evening, worried and torn by indecision, the Vernons struggled with their fears. Barbara maintained her position that they should step aside from the program while continuing to help when and where they were able to. Hildy was more concerned with the direct and immediate effects in their lives if they stayed with Merrill. Back and forth they argued and reasoned. And finally, they prayed for guidance and help.

At one in the morning, exhausted, they went to bed.

14

Norm Todd, financial head of Don Turner's three automobile dealerships, was known for fast decisions.

"What we have to do, Don, is close this big store immediately and combine things with our small West Rockfort location. We're losing our shirts. Over there, people are still buying our imports. We can get by. We'll get rid of twenty-five people in sales, service, parts and the office."

"We've been in business here for twenty years!"

"So what? Sales are dead. Profits there ain't."

"How do we know Detroit will go along with a move? Fred Schaeffer has people ready to buy our franchise."

"I can handle Schaeffer."

"I don't like to quit."

"Then for God's sake get off the religious kick! Listen, Don, let me put out the bait! Full-color pages, a weekend tent sale, free coffee and donuts, a prize drawing. Promise 'em anything." He jumped up, waving his arms in the air. "Every car must go! Bring us your best deal and we'll beat it by five hundred bucks! No gimmicks! No low-balls! No add-ons! No fooling! Win a Florida vacation for two! They'll eat it up!"

"You know that kind of ad is misleading."

"Who's misleading who? What are *you* doing? What's that jerk of a preacher doing? Promising folks they get a free ticket to heaven? You're costing people their jobs, man! Merrill oughta pack it in and get out!"

When Don Turner was silent, Todd went on. "You know what? Let me tell you something. I'm selling my stake in Don Turner motors. To the highest bidder. You can sit here alone and read your prayer book and rot!" He slammed the door on his way out.

15

An hour later, Turner picked up his wife and they headed for the rectory. "I can't go on," he said.

"What is it now?"

"Todd wants me to close the Boulevard location. Move everything to the West side. He threatens to sell his share of the business for whatever he can get."

"What would that mean?"

"One thing. Detroit will cancel me out. Todd is a hustler. They all know that."

"He'd join a new franchise owner at your place?"

"Of course. They'd be crazy not to take him."

They drove in silence. At the rectory, Ann Merrill answered the bell. She pointed to the study and hurried away without a word.

"What can we do?" Sara Turner asked tearfully.

Her husband described Todd's idea to resume deceptive advertising and his threat to sell his interest in the business.

"That's very bad," Merrill agreed.

"I believe in your program, Will," Don said. "But maybe it just won't work. Not today. Not in my business, anyway. I want to stick with you. But, I don't see—I really don't see how I can."

Merrill paused and looked at them, his face lined with worry and concern for his friends. At last he said: "Let's begin by praying together." They knelt in prayer for several minutes.

When Merrill paused, Turner asked: "I hear everything you've said but how can I use it? What can I do right now, Will, to head off this catastrophe? Tell me, what can I do?"

The minister replied: "I don't have an easy answer. I wish I did. We will find a way. *You* will find the way. You will because Jesus loves you and His way is your way. You're important to Jesus. Remember that, Don. Believe."

He opened the Bible and read Luke 11:9-10. *And I say to you, ask, and it shall be given you; seek, and ye shall find; knock, and it shall be opened unto you. For every one that asketh receiveth and he that seeketh findeth; and to him that knocketh it shall be opened.*

"We are told that we must ask, we must seek and we must

135

knock," the minister explained. "It won't just happen. We won't find, we won't receive unless we do something. We must ask, we must seek, we must knock. That means one thing: we must have faith, we must believe. We don't ask with faint hope. We don't knock gently, doubting that the door will open. We must know! We must believe!" He reached out and touched Don Turner's arm. "Then it will happen."

The car dealer sighed and was silent.

Merrill asked: "How much longer can you hang on? Before you actually have to give up your Boulevard location?"

Turner shrugged. "Hard to say. A few weeks, I suppose. Maybe with luck, two months."

"Let's give it a try, then. Two months." He held out his hand. "Is that a bargain?"

"Yes."

On the drive home, Don Turner said. "We're risking everything we have. We could close up now and move, the way Todd said. Save something. In two months it could be too late."

Sara Turner looked at her husband. "We promised Merrill. We can't go back on that." She smiled at him. "I'm with you, if you'll try."

"I've already tried," Turner said gloomily. "And failed."

16

The strike at East-West lines was in full force. Angry pickets marched in front of the main building, carrying posters that proclaimed "Unfair Rules."

Reverend Merrill almost made it to the entrance to Wes McLain's office but his way was blocked by rough, enraged workers. Mel Prosser, the union boss who had flown in from Chicago, stood nearby.

"Get lost, preacher!" the men shouted. "Bug off, man!"

"None of that Bible stuff here!" "Back to Church where you belong!"

Two police officers on duty cleared the way for Merrill. The minister found Wes McLain, morose and bewildered, at his desk. "I don't know what to do," McLain said. "It all happened so fast. Prosser came in last night. They went out at seven this morning."

"I'm going back down and talk to them," Merrill said.

"No, you can't."

"I must."

"There's no telling what they might do."

"They'll be all right. The police are here."

McLain shook his head. "Then I'm going with you."

They moved to a platform on the edge of the building and the crowd slowly changed its marching course to gather in front of McLain and the minister.

Willard Merrill held up his right hand. Gradually the crowd quieted down.

"Our only purpose in being here is to speak to you of the word of God." There were boos, catcalls. "We seek to hurt no one, only to help!" There were more yells of defiance, obscenities. Merrill persisted. "You men are engaged in useful, important work. You know and understand the value of work. And so do we. It says in Psalm 90:17 *Let the beauty of the Lord our God be upon us: and establish thou the work of our hands upon us...*

"You have a right to fair wages, good working conditions. But you don't have a right to walk off the job and resort to violence! I plead with you to go back to work while your leaders mediate!"

The shouts increased. Someone threw a soda can. Others picked up pieces of broken cement and stones and threw them at McLain and Merrill. Prosser shouted for the men to stop. The police rushed the crowd. But two officers were not nearly enough. The crowd was out of control. A beer bottle struck Merrill on the forehead. He staggered and McLain grabbed him, preventing him from falling.

Suddenly the crowd was quiet. The police tried to push through to seize the man who had thrown the bottle but he was lost in the surging mob. One of the cops ran to the platform and helped Merrill step down. He escorted the minister through the crowd to his car. McLain was at Merrill's side, supporting him. They managed to get into the car, with McLain at the wheel. The car was backing to make a turn when the strikers rushed at the vehicle. They smashed the rear window. A dozen men, pushing and lifting, almost tipped the car over before the police beat them back. Finally, McLain maneuvered the car clear of the strike area.

He drove Merrill to the hospital where six stitches were needed for the gash in the minister's head. When he was released, McLain drove him to the rectory. Ann was not at home. McLain found an ice bag, filled it and stayed until Merrill was stretched out on the living room sofa, the ice bag in place. The minister smiled up at him. "Could've been worse."

"Hardly."

McLain phoned for a taxi to take him back to the office. In the cab, he struggled with himself. Over and over again he asked: How can I go on? What am I doing that is wrong? Dear Jesus, I don't know what to do. I'm trying but I'm afraid. I'm afraid. I never felt this way before. Later, returning home in his own car he gripped the wheel until his knuckles were white.

Grimly he stared at the dark road ahead.

Was it worth it?

17

Sam Ott was a frail man in his late fifties, with thin graying hair, soft blue eyes and a ready smile. He waited until Marsha Hoyt put down the phone.

"Miss Hoyt, I been coming to the mission for about a week now."

"Yes, Sam, I've seen you."

"You work so hard, all the time." The man searched for words. "I been off the stuff for two months now, could I—I mean, I'd like to help. Work with some of these kids that's hooked. I already talked to some of them. I could help them."

"Quit drugs, you mean?"

"Yes. Tell them what I went through, how I beat it. This would make it easier when the social worker comes in."

"We need a drug abuse program."

"I'll get it going for you."

"Thank you, Sam."

It was the second new volunteer in as many days. Jake Clark, a fat, jovial alcoholic had asked to start meetings two nights a week with someone from Alcoholics Anonymous. Marsha and Virginia now had eight volunteers, each devoting at least four days a week to the mission.

Among them was a young blond girl, Loretta Sims, who was trying to escape prostitution; she helped in the kitchen. And a derelict brought in by Jake Clark slept in the dorm and cleaned the shower room. The volunteers asked nothing; they existed from day to day, sharing a common ground of feelings and surroundings.

Again and again they voiced their feelings. "This place made me believe," was the way Sam Ott put it. Jake Clark, his dark eyes unwavering, said simply: "I believe. I believe in Jesus." Another insisted, "Jesus saved me." All were adamant in vowing: "I don't want to go back out there!"

They idolized Ginny and Marsha and were anxious to please them. They waited patiently to be given tasks to perform, making beds, washing dishes and windows. No job was too menial.

In only four weeks the House of Jesus had blossomed. By actual count, 14 individuals insisted they had been converted

139

to Jesus. These 14 visited the mission each day; others occupied the dorms. They were shining examples to the 60 or 70 who drifted in and out every day, participating in events, reading or resting.

One week's attendance figures showed many benefiting from activities:

Seniors:	Crafts, games	− 122
	Reading room	− 184
Youth:	Reading, writing	− 30
	Bible lessons	− 18
Drug abuse:		− 8
Alcohol		− 12
Family Counseling:		− 8

Up to 100 light meals were served each day. An average of 28 persons were accommodated in the dorms every night.

The young blond girl, Loretta Sims, became attached to Virginia Carver. Loretta had managed to flee from an escort service, a thin front for prostitution, but she was hopelessly addicted to cocaine and whiskey. Slowly, without too much pressure, Virginia induced Loretta to sit in on drug and alcohol sessions, and to attend Reverend Merrill's regular weekly talk at the mission.

On a Thursday late in September, the meeting room at the House of Jesus was packed; an overflow crowd swarmed at the doorway and stood under the open windows. The minister launched his strongest attack yet on the forces of evil.

"They said it couldn't be done! They said we'd be beaten back, compelled to give up. Sin City would throw us out! But it hasn't happened, my friends!" He gave a brief summary of attendance at mission activities. "I say to you, vice and sin, crime and corruption in our city will go! We've made our start. But it is only a start! The big job is ahead of us. We ask you

140

to join us. Bring your husbands, your wives, your children, your relatives, your neighbors. Together we will chase out those who sell sin and destruction. We will do it, my friends! In the words of Luke 1:37: *For with God nothing shall be impossible.*"

Merrill introduced Roger Heath, of Lincoln College, the candidate for mayor pledged to clean up Sin City.

Then Marsha Hoyt sang Horatius Bonar's hymn.

> I heard the voice of Jesus say
> > Come unto me and rest;
> Lay down, thou weary one, lay down
> > Thy head upon my breast.
> I came to Jesus as I was,
> > Weary, and worn, and sad;
> I found in Him a resting-place,
> > And He has made me glad.

Throughout the service, Mort Freel and Lennie Grob had stood in the rear, silent and expressionless. When the hymn ended the two mobsters elbowed their way to the street.

"Get him!" Freel barked.

Slowly, many in the audience filed out. Some lingered at the coffee service and the regulars moved into reading and game rooms. It was after nine o'clock when Willard Merrill said to Professor Heath: "I'll drop you off. I have to get back to the parsonage."

They went out to the small parking area between the mission and the north wing of the old machine-tool plant. Merrill's car was between a gray van and a wire fence that surrounded the lot. He had his keys in the door lock when it happened. A large man hit Merrill in the back of the head, turned him around and drove his other fist into the minister's stomach. Roger Heath, also struck from behind, was sprawled on the ground. He struggled to get to his feet. Merrill attempted to fight back. There were three men, unrecognizable in the dimly lit area. For perhaps 12 seconds they battled. Heath shouted "Help! Police!" He was again knocked to the ground.

141

Another man appeared. "Hey! What is this?" he yelled and tore into the hoodlums. He shoved one of the attackers away and the fellow slipped and went down on one knee. He grabbed the shoulders of another and pulled him away from Merrill. Suddenly a light on the side of the building came on. The three men fled.

"My God! It's Will Merrill!"

The minister straightened up.

"Jerry Carver!"

"What's this all about?"

"They didn't like my talk, I guess."

With Jerry driving Merrill's car they went to Doctor Egbert's home. The minister, with painfully sore ribs, preferred not to return to the hospital so soon after the bottle-throwing incident.

"Let's also keep the media out of this one," he decided. "The *Herald* had a field day with the gash in my head."

Merrill and Heath, with minor cuts and bruises, were examined and treated by Doctor Egbert.

"You've got to be careful, Will," the doctor cautioned. "These people are criminals. Next time you may not be so lucky. Now go home and rest."

Jerry drove the minister to the parsonage. At the door he said: "Reverend, I've seen enough to be on your side. I believe in you. I went to the mission tonight to see how Ginny and Marsha were getting along. Lucky for me I arrived at a good time. From now on, I'm with you, with what you're trying to do."

Willard Merrill beamed, held out his hand.

"Thank you, Jerry. We certainly can use you."

In his study, the minister offered a prayer of thanksgiving for his new recruit, and for the fact that no one was hurt more seriously.

Jerry Carver climbed into his sports car and headed home. He felt a glow of satisfaction over his part in the incident. It was a good feeling. He had done something really worthwhile for someone.

October

1

The story in the *Wall Street Journal* shook Rockfort's Committee of Fifty. Nothing in the city's history had ever caused such excitement. A hastily called luncheon, attended by most of the membership, was a clash of gossip and speculation.

"When was the reporter here?" an attorney asked.

"He spent several days here, left over the weekend," someone answered.

"Most of the time with Merrill, and at the mission. By the way, I didn't know Merrill was attacked getting into his car. There was nothing in the paper."

"He was hit by a bottle at the East-West strike."

"No. This came after. He was beaten up outside the mission, too."

"You're kidding!"

A real estate man cut in. "This town's getting a bad name." He read from the *Wall Street Journal* story. "'The minister's drive against crime appears to be well-founded. A survey in East Rockfort, once a thriving industrial area but now known locally as Sin City, turned up nude bars, smoke shops openly selling drugs, at least two gambling establishments and three houses of prostitution.'"

"That story hurts us," a builder asserted. "I've been working for six months with Chicago money that's ready to build a condo on the old Bingham property. The guy called this morning and put the deal on hold."

"Why? Because of this article?"

"Yeah. He read it. His partners read it. They decided to wait and see."

An insurance man spoke up. "The reporter didn't miss much. He covered McLain's strike. And how in hell did he find out Don Turner's in all that trouble with his Boulevard place?"

"A good reporter finds out everything."

"What triggered this story?"

"All the press coverage Merrill's been getting. The A.P. and U.P. both had stories a couple of weeks ago."

"I don't like it," the attorney said. "This will make Sin City sound worse than it is. The story says cars and noisy motorcycle gangs from out of state have been spotted in the area late at night. Not far from some of our pretty good neighborhoods."

"What's City Hall doing?"

"Nothing."

"Merrill's pushing Heath for mayor."

"He hasn't got a chance. And it's better for us to keep things as they are."

"If I know anything about Heath, he'll give it his best shot."

"A professor? Forget it."

The builder rose and stood by his chair. "We could use Heath," he said quietly, drawing several strange looks.

A banker said: "Maybe you guys don't realize what's happened down there. The population of East Rockfort is down seventeen percent in ten years. And their unemployment rate is nineteen percent!"

"This stink will make it worse," the builder said. "My new condo would've been only a half mile from Sin City, in that wooded stretch along the river." He walked away.

An attorney slapped the table with the folded *Journal.* "They make it sound like Ed Vernon's *News* is going belly up."

Most of the men left the dining room to hurry back to their offices. A small group lingered at one of the tables and drank coffee. "They did a good job on the Carvers and Marsha Hoyt, too," the insurance man said. "Listen: 'Two attractive

144

young women, Virginia Carver, the heiress, and Marsha Hoyt, a church soloist, are running a shelter for the poor and the elderly in an abandoned factory. They work seven days a week.'"

And there's more: "'The second attack on Reverend Merrill, allegedly by persons allied with Sin City's criminal elements, occurred in the mission parking lot. The minister was aided by Gerald Carver, brother of Virginia Carver, both heirs to the fortune left by multi-millionaire Alfred J. Carver. Hey, this is beginning to sound like *Dynasty!*"

Throughout the luncheon, Rodney Brent had remained strangely silent. Now and then he had added a brief comment but he was not the outspoken, confident bank chairman his friends knew so well. Abruptly he said his goodbyes and left. Rodney Brent really didn't care what happened in Sin City. He had come to the luncheon to get out of his office, away from bad loans, away from the Cleveland loan. But it hadn't helped. He could no longer hide the truth.

The Cleveland loan, all $12 million of it, was in full default.

2

Roger Heath's campaign for mayor of Rockfort started late and was a desperate uphill battle. The political machine in power was backed by the Establishment, which included the City Club and the Committee of Fifty. And of course it was vigorously supported by the mob, the men who controlled drugs, gambling, prostitution, illegal alcohol. Their stranglehold on Sin City provided funds to aid in the re-election of Mayor Harold Tuttle and the current councilmen and commissioners.

Ellen Heath was a tireless worker for her husband's cause. She organized fund-raising teams, took care of printing, posters and direct-mail lists. She leased a vacant store, installed telephones, desks, and rented a Xerox machine. Roger Heath, granted a leave of absence by Lincoln College, based his campaign on stamping out crime in East Rockfort, on slum clearance and a rebuilding program to attract new industry and housing to the area.

"The *News* gave you good coverage on your talk at the Garden Club lunch," Ellen said late one afternoon.

"We can always count on Ed Vernon," Roger Heath said. "The *Herald,* unfortunately, is on Tuttle's side, all the way."

"You're not getting discouraged?"

"No," he said with a sudden burst of enthusiasm. "Not when we have Will Merrill with us, and the entire staff at the college. They're wonderful."

"They sent over a nice contribution," Ellen said.

"If we only had enough money to afford television and radio spots."

"We will. I know we will."

He smiled at his wife. "I wouldn't dream of making this try without you."

Wherever he went, on street corners, at fraternal and organization meetings, at a rally held at the Rockfort Women's Club, there was interest and apparent support; but far too many who heard the professor were openly skeptical. How could this man, educated, attractive and a fine speaker but admittedly a novice at politics, expect to win? He would be swamped by Harold Tuttle's in-depth constituency, by tens of thousands who saw Tuttle as an able public official with a good record in extracting funds from the state capital and from Washington.

Extensive road repairs, a waste cleanup effort, renovations at the Wellington High School were started just before the campaign. If there was crime and corruption in a few places, and if Sin City was a disgrace, that was because the entire country was awash in crime. It was Washington's fault.

146

The governor's fault. Don't blame Hal. He's a good guy.

Roger Heath was booed when he spoke in working-class neighborhoods. Blue-collar citizens, though their number had been sharply reduced over the past few years, were allied to the machine through habit. They were quick to put down the man from Lincoln College—a "do-gooder"—representing little old ladies and reformers. And with the backing of that bunch of weirdos at the Pleasant Valley Church. Jesus freaks.

They didn't admit it but even many of Heath's most ardent supporters felt that their man had no chance. Evil would triumph over good, as usual.

Mort Freel and Lennie Grob saw the college man as a troublemaker who ought to stay in his own back yard.

"You say he ain't gotta chance," Mort Freel argued at a meeting upstairs at the Key West. "I say we don't know *what* the crumb might do. You say the guy's already lost the election. Maybe. Maybe not. The bum might win in a photo finish."

"Naw," Lennie protested.

"We don't coast like it was nuthin'! We invested a lot of time and money. Things is runnin' real smooth now."

One of Freel's lieutenants spoke up. "The teacher takes his orders from preacher man, don't he? Only a couple dozen jerks care what that guy says."

Mort Freel glared at the underling. "You should count so good! He packs 'em in at the mission every time he opens his trap." Mort Freel lit a cigar. "Listen. I don't want no antsy-pantsy school teacher in the race. I want him out."

"How?" Lennie asked.

"You tell *me*, genius."

Lennie Grob thought for a moment. "You don't want him, he's gotta go."

"You got it."

"It'll look funny. When he's runnin' for office and all."

"Make it so it don't look funny. Real natural."

Lennie stared down at the floor.

147

Freel took a drag on his cigar and blew a cloud of smoke at the other two.

"Our boy Heath's not alone."

Lennie Grob blinked. "Naw, his wife's with him, and a mob of kids and some cruds from the college. They don't mean nothin'."

Freel snorted. "You blind or something?"

"Why? What?"

"We don't touch kids and big brains. We go to the top, stupid."

The lieutenant looked at Lennie and grinned. "The preacher?"

Mort Freel nodded, glowered. "You messed it up last time. Don't louse it up again, understand?"

3

Loretta Sims collapsed at the mission a few moments after Reverend Merrill's regular Thursday evening sermon. She had been standing in the archway between the large meeting hall and the reading room. Loretta was nineteen, a lovely girl with a captivating smile and gray-green eyes.

Merrill rushed to her side and helped to revive her. She was taken to a quiet section of the room where the minister prayed for her and offered encouragement.

"You've worked hard to help us here at the mission," he said. "Now it's our turn to help you."

"Nobody can do anything," she said listlessly.

"Give us a chance. Give Jesus a chance to enter your life. He is ready, always there. All He asks is your faith. Your faith in Him. Think of it this way. You enter this room. It is dark. You reach out to the light switch and turn it on. You instantly have light. Now, what did that take? Your faith! Belief in pushing the switch. You never doubted for a second. You knew. That was enough. It is the same way in our work. If we just have faith, if we know that the switch is there, waiting for us to act, we can be certain that we will have light. Light which is the love of Jesus filling our lives."

Loretta Sims looked up at him, wide-eyed, as if this friendly man with iron-gray hair was someone she'd never seen before.

"But you understand all that."

"Yes, and it's there for you, too, Loretta," the minister said quietly. "It's not ours alone. It's yours, too. I want you to let us help you." She frowned and he went on. "No, I don't mean books and study and classes. Just pray with us. Make your decision to turn your back on yesterday, forget the past. God does not seek recompense; He forgives. Come with us. I promise you, you will start a new life. You are so young. You will have a happy life."

To Loretta, with no relatives and few friends it was difficult to believe that this man was actually saying he would help her.

Loretta had been used and abused since she was fourteen. Men had always taken from her. Her body. Her time. Her money in exchange for drugs and alcohol. When she was sick from too much cocaine and rum, what had they done? Called First Aid and walked away. She had been revived, treated, and sent back to life in a sleazy furnished room and the bars of Sin City. Only at the House of Jesus, in these few weeks, had Loretta Sims known friendship from people who wanted to give, not take.

Tears came to her eyes and she slowly shook her head in disbelief. Merrill smiled at her, tried to make her comfortable in an arm chair. But suddenly, as in a trance, the girl rose and started toward the door. She was almost out of the room when she staggered and grasped the archway. Virginia Carver rushed to her side and kept her from falling.

"I'm driving her to Dr. Egbert's," Virginia said. "She hasn't looked right all week."

149

After an examination, Les Egbert gave his diagnosis. "Nothing too serious that I can see. A slow pulse. Blood pressure down. Underweight. A slight fever. Needs rest and three good meals a day."

Virginia Carver made her decision on the spot. She took Loretta to the Carver mansion and gave her a huge room and bath on the second floor. In three days, Loretta was stronger, the fever was gone. She insisted on returning to help out at the mission.

Virginia agreed. "But you'll stay with us while you decide what to do. If you want to go back to school, think about a career in something, computers, maybe. Your home is with us."

Jerry Carver was helpful and often drove Loretta to the mission or home again. "The kid is very bright," he told Virginia one day. "How'd she ever get into prostitution? I can see her holding down a good job."

Geraldine Carver was less enthusiastic. "Ginny," she announced, "it's all well and good to save a lost soul if you can but we don't have to turn over the house to this girl. Her room is always a mess. She sits in front of television until two in the morning. She leaves her cigarette butts all over the place."

"Give her a chance, Deeny," Ginny said, smiling. "She can't become a saint overnight. And who'd want her to? The girl's never had a chance. Parents took off when she was eight. Lived with a grandmother for a few years, then took to the streets."

"That's my point. We're not supposed to take in people off the streets. That's what you have your mission for. God knows, you've poured enough money into that place without opening a branch in your own home!"

"It's only one girl, Deeny."

"The servants are upset. The girl is so sloppy."

"She'll improve, Deeny," Jerry said.

"Maybe so. But at my age I don't have the energy to watch."

"She's clean," he added.

"I should hope so! She takes three showers a day!"

"So what? She's washing away the past," Jerry said.

"Will Merrill's working with her. He says she's made great progress. Comes to church, seems to be determined to turn her life around. I want her to settle on a career and stay here with us while she decides what to do."

Geraldine Carver shrugged. "Exactly as you please. It's your home." Her lips firmed. "But don't come crying to me if she steals our best silver." She went to the door and turned back. "This is all too much for me. I'm leaving tomorrow on a short cruise to the Bahamas. Betty Jane has been after me for months to go with her."

November

1

Arnold Grimsley stood at the window in his luxurious office high above Michigan Boulevard and stared out at the lake, choppy now in the stiff breeze on the first day in November.

He went back to his ornate desk and picked up the copy of the *Wall Street Journal* he had kept. He read the story through for the third time.

Arnold Grimsley sat back and reflected.

It was time now to clean up neglected things. Another year was rushing to a close.

A minister down in Rockfort sets the city on its ear with his call to the ways of Jesus. What happens? Strikes. Beatings. Protests. With the help of a few believers the man of God opens a mission. He perseveres. Trouble. Resistance. Obstacles. Still he carries on.

It brought to Arnold Grimsley thoughts of his own early years. The struggles. The obstacles. The defeats. And, finally, the victories. Grimsley had been broke at 22, rich at 30, broke again at 43. Then, using what he'd learned the hard way, he'd risen to great wealth, the major stockholder in six multi-national companies. He again picked up the *Wall Street Journal* and stared at the story without reading it.

He buzzed his secretary and asked not to be disturbed. Then Grimsley slowly roamed about his huge office. Do as Jesus would do, Merrill says. All right in Rockfort, but—here in Chicago? Could it be? What if I had lived my life as a follower of Jesus? Would I be here now? Would I have a penthouse apartment a few miles to the north? Apartments in New

York, London, Paris? I have everything, really. I spend much of my spare time reading. What else is there? I hate sports. I like the theatre and opera but that's about it. And I don't like to go alone. I guess if I were to admit it, I'm lonely. But that's only part of it. Life has been rewarding—but it's been unfulfilling. There's something missing. Missing. What is it?

Without realizing he was doing it, as if guided by an unseen power, Arnold Grimsley slowly sank to his knees. For the first time in his life, he prayed. He prayed for understanding of what that minister in Indiana was trying to do. He prayed for understanding of the void in his life that seemed to increase as he grew older. Then Arnold Grimsley rose, feeling a certain peace, an unexpected comfort.

He called his secretary and dictated a letter.

2

Willard Merrill could not shake his feeling of impending disaster. It was the result of days and nights of worry and doubt. Worry over carrying things too far and causing his loyal followers so much trouble. Doubt that he had chosen the right course. Maybe the whole thing was one vast mistake, a tragic error in judgment. His own life was in chaos. His wife had scarcely spoken to him in a week.

True, the House of Jesus was going well. Marsha and Virginia were deep into plans for Thanksgiving. Loretta Sims appeared to be making progress. But those bright spots were heavily overshadowed by acute problems almost too numerous to consider.

They went beyond the distress of his close friends, the scorn of business leaders, the coolness he had encountered on a recent visit to the City Club. As an honorary member, he was not a club regular but now he was aware of

153

a change; he felt he was no longer welcome at the club.

What am I to do? Merrill asked himself. I've come so far, and yet the road becomes rougher each day. I've prayed so hard. And for what? I've injured my dear friends!

Oh, Jesus, help me, help me! Trembling in confusion now, the minister knelt beside his desk. He lifted his eyes and spoke aloud. Jesus, there is a way, there is a way to overcome. I cannot go on bringing misery to others. What am I doing that is wrong? Show me the way, oh Lord. Lead me in thy steps. Give me the wisdom to know what is right and the courage to follow You. Help me to love my neighbor.

He rose, sat silently in his chair for a long time, fighting to bring his tortured thoughts under control. At last he reached for one of his favorite books and opened it to W.O. Cushing's hymn, *Follow On.*

> Down in the valley with my Savior I would go,
> Where the storms are sweeping and dark waters flow;
> With His hand to lead me I will never, never fear;
> Danger cannot fight me if my Lord is near.
> For I know, whatever befall me,
> Jesus doeth all things well.

He read the hymn three times before he heard a letter slide under the door to his study. He picked it up, opened it. It was from an Arnold Grimsley in Chicago. It was a letter of praise and encouragement. It ended with "Carry on!" Something fell out of the envelope to the floor. He picked it up. It was a check. The Reverend's hands shook when he saw the amount. $50,000.

His spirits soaring, the minister went to his desk and began to prepare his Sunday sermon.

3

As if spurred by Arnold Grimsley's generosity, Willard Merrill spoke on giving. The congregation was not as large as it had been. The weather had been cold and rainy and many regulars were now content to listen to the service on radio.

"It is more blessed to give than to receive. That's what the Bible tells us. It doesn't say when you receive you'd better give, just to be on the safe side. No. You must give! First!

"We can't always give money. But we can *give.* We can give things that count far more than money. We can give understanding, praise, encouragement. We can give joy, a smile, laughter. We can give these things if we're flat broke.

"Let us resolve now to give to others by helping, by being considerate, unselfish, loving. Where? Look around you. Your family, friends. On the job. People need you. Come work with us in Sin City. We have hundreds of the unfortunate who need help. Come and see what miracles your giving can bring about."

Marsha Hoyt sang the words of Stephen Foster.

Ask and it shall be given,
Seek and ye shall find,
Every prayer is heard in heaven
That is breathed from a truthful mind.

Every prayer is heard above
That we sincerely feel,
Every sigh received with love,
When we repenting kneel.

Later, in the Activities Hall, at the weekly group meeting, the mood was downcast. Arnold Grimsley's letter and check brought a slight upturn in spirits. But the small attendance, the widespread knowledge of Vernon's, Turner's and McLain's troubles and the problems all were experiencing in their personal lives combined to dampen the usual enthusiasm of the group.

As Willard Merrill went to his home he was both elated and troubled. Elated because he knew there would be real

155

benefits from the unexpected donation from Arnold Grimsley. Troubled because there was something bleak and unsettling about the raw November day. The election was almost at hand. So much depended on Roger Heath. His chances appeared slim. The few pollsters who bothered to take a count gave Heath no chance at all. Without him, how could the machine that ran between City Hall and Sin City ever be derailed?

The week to come would be disquieting at best.

Reverend Merrill went to his study. Almost too distracted to pray, he forced himself to open the Bible. He turned once more to one of his favorite Psalms, the 46th.

God is our refuge and strength, a very present help in trouble. If ever he was in trouble and needed help, it was now.

Therefore will not we fear, though the earth be removed, and though the mountains be carried into the midst of the sea. Could anything be more catastrophic than that? His own life was catastrophic, being swept away to destruction.

God is in the midst of her; she shall not be moved: God shall help her, and that right early... Was that not a call to his faith?

God shall help her! What could be more precise?

The Lord of hosts is with us: the God of Jacob is our refuge.. He is with me now! the minister said aloud. If only I will accept Him!

Be still and know that I am God: I will be exalted among the heathen, I will be exalted in the earth. It was all there. So clear. It was Willard Merrill's only hope.

Grim, pale, the minister knelt in prayer.

The phone on his desk rang three times before he answered it. Merrill, unaware of how long he had been in prayer, mumbled an almost incoherent, "Hello."

"This is Val Hudson, producer of *60 Minutes,* the Sunday night show on CBS."

"Yes," Merrill said.

Hudson continued: "We've read about you, heard about you, seen the *Wall Street Journal* story. We might be interested in doing a piece on you. Could some of our people fly out there and spend some time with you?"

Almost because he couldn't fight anymore, because he couldn't say "no," Willard Merrill murmured, "All right, if you want to. Anytime."

4

Ed Vernon had concealed the truth from his wife, Barbara. She had no idea of the money he had spent in the losing battle to keep the *News* afloat.

Ev Marno, his treasurer, knew that something like $185,000 of Vernon's personal assets had been poured in, only to dissolve in the onrushing tide of red ink.

Vernon studied the calendar on his cluttered desk. It was November second. By the end of January, if things continued on their dreadful course, he would be flat broke. It was a frightening prospect. A 53-year-old publishing executive was unlikely to be swamped with job offers. Why had he allowed things to go so far down hill? There had been a time, in the early days of Will Merrill's program, when the *News* could have been put back on course, its readership and advertising restored to the old levels. Now it was too late.

Ed Vernon had ignored his father's warning: "Eddie, this paper can give you a fine living, everything you want, as long as it's healthy. But if it starts to go, if things turn down, never jump in with your own money."

Dana Bell approached through the half-deserted newsroom. "I'm sorry, Ed," the managing editor said quietly. "This is my last day."

When Vernon did not answer, Bell sat and continued. "I'm going over to the *Herald.* They're doing real good right now. I'll be editing their new weekend edition."

157

"I understand," Vernon said. "I've let you down. I've let everybody down. I don't know why."

"Look, you did what you had to do. It's your paper. You can do whatever you want."

"No. I can't. I have responsibilities. I wasn't realistic. I went off into fantasy land. The real world out there is tough, Dana, it doesn't sit around waiting while you explore the magic kingdom."

"We make mistakes."

"Look what I've done. All these people we let go! The price of the stock is way off—nobody wants it. I've hurt others, Dana, that's what's so bad."

"You paid the last dividend out of your own pocket, I know that."

"Yes." Ed Vernon rose and came around to Bell's chair. "Dana, we've been together a long time. You're a great newspaper man. I'll make up to you what you've lost in this mess. Every nickel. And the same for the other shareholders. If it's the last thing I do." He paused thoughtfully. "I've a new idea to throw at Joel Watkins. Maybe we can pull in some new ads."

Dana Bell was on his feet. "Ed, Joel's gone. To the *Herald*. He told me this morning." Bell hesitated, his real concern for Ed Vernon wrinkling his forehead. "Brad Steever, too. The *Herald's* off and running on circulation. Brad got a good deal."

They shook hands and Dana Bell was gone.

There wasn't any new idea, Vernon told himself. It had been a desperate attempt to stall, to make believe, a floundering hope that by some miracle he could turn back.

Maybe it would be best to shut down the *News*. Right now. Not wait till the end of the month.

5

This location closed. Visit us at Third Avenue and Broad Street. The sign in the window of Turner Motors shocked old customers. "Joe Mathews, their best salesman, got out." "The good mechanics quit." "Turner's on some religious kick with that minister." "Strange!"

The Monday morning mail from Detroit was no surprise. "Your franchise with us, expiring December 1, will not be renewed."

Without a word to anyone, Don Turner got into his car and headed for Forest Drive along the north side of the lake. The road would be deserted at this hour. Turner had always been able to think through his problems while at the wheel. Even in the heaviest traffic, he could get a new perspective, a fresh slant on a difficult situation. It was as if he'd been born to drive a car. He'd learned at 17. In high school he was called upon to drive the principal through the heaviest snows to out-of-town basketball games. At 18, he'd done most of the driving on a trip with his parents to California. If you wanted to know anything about cars, you asked Don Turner. "That kid lives for cars!"

He'd gone directly from high school to a job selling used cars. Then on to new Buicks. Within three years he was the top salesman at the dealership. Soon his record was one of the best in the country. Don Turner, affable, smiling, well-dressed, often told himself that he was the best salesman anywhere. His income was proof enough. He and Sara had lived well, entertained lavishly, enjoyed the good life.

Turner stopped the car where a huge rock formation jutted out into the lake. It was a perfect place to sit, get some sun or simply enjoy the sound of the water lapping at the shore.

His second dealership would have to close. The factory in Europe was even unhappier than Detroit. There was a waiting list of well-financed, would-be dealers ready to pay almost

159

anything for a good franchise,men who had seen established dealers pile up millions.

Don Turner knew he still could make a living. His remaining showroom and service shop would keep him solvent. He'd go back to selling. It was the contraction that hurt, being a little guy again, a fringe operator trying to make it with a low-volume brand.

Give up the cruiser, Don, the big parties, the trips to Hawaii, Barbados, Europe. Sell the condominium in the islands. Sara will adjust. She'll understand. She's been concerned for some time about their rich but empty life.

Was this really happening?

What about Don Turner himself? A super salesman at 25. Washed up at 44. For the first time in his life, he had no new ideas, no fresh slants, no determination to win. For the next 15 minutes he threw stones out into the lake. Then he got into his car.

Don Turner was numb. His mind was a blank. He had no idea of what to do, where to go.

6

It wasn't unusual for the president of Intra, Ltd. to stop off in Rockfort four or five times a year. As the head of a corporation that owned half a dozen companies, including East-West Lines, Kirk Norwood flew all over the Midwest in his own plane. What made today's visit different was that Norwood had phoned at 6 A.M. and ordered Wes McLain to go to the airport and wait. No arrival time was mentioned.

The strike had ended and operations were almost normal at the terminal but McLain was aware of the underlying friction that persisted among the men. There was grumbling.

Hostile glances. Workers called in sick. To maintain schedules, overtime was up. That cost money. And Kirk Norwood liked money.

The twin Beechcraft touched down at 10:18. It was too early for lunch. McLain had visualized a drive to his office, a talk, then lunch at the Bristol Cafe. Afterward, he would take Norwood back to his plane.

"Let's go in the coffee shop," Kirk Norwood said flatly, leading the way. He was a man of perhaps 50, medium height, partially bald, wearing gold-rimmed glasses. "I have to be in Indianapolis for lunch."

It took eight minutes. Norwood said: "We have to make a change, Wes. We're bringing Stu Brady over from Kansas City to take charge here. You're finished. You know what's been going on better than I do. I'm sorry. You were a good manager. Then something happened to you."

"But—"

"It's that simple, Wes. Accounting will contact you."

He stood up, grabbed the check and headed for the cashier with a shaken McLain close behind him. At Gate E, leading to the private plane ramp, he stopped abruptly. "Don't come out with me. Stu will be here tomorrow. Show him what he needs to know."

It didn't take McLain long to clean out his desk. He discarded old papers and arranged current work in neat stacks for Stu Brady. When he had finished, he stood back and surveyed the office. Ten years of his life. Good years for the most part. A raise every 18 months. Annual bonus checks. Watching the operation grow. Running things his own way. All gone now. What would he do? What could he do? Wes McLain closed the door and went down to his car. He sat behind the wheel. He tried to pray but couldn't concentrate. He kept thinking of Alice and Jeff. How long could he avoid telling them? What was the point? He couldn't spend his days riding

161

around, making believe he was at work. Face them. Have it over with.

It was two-thirty when he arrived home. Alice was watching her soap opera. Jeff had come in from school moments before.

"What are you home now for?" the boy inquired.

Wes waited until the program was over. Then he told them.

"Hell, Pop, they can't do that to you!"

Alice was grim. "It's that Jesus thing! The strike. Smashed windows. All this business with that minister. How could you do a thing like this to me and Jeff!"

"Alice—"

"What are we supposed to do now? Jeff has another year at school. What about college? I guess that's out, now. Do you expect me to go to work?"

"I'll get a job."

"At what? A night watchman, like Collinson down the street? He's only forty-nine and that's all he could get."

"Pop can go back to driving a truck."

"Sure!" Alice said scornfully. "At half the pay he was making. Besides, he's too old. We got a big mortgage on this place, don't forget that!"

"Why don't you both look on the bright side?" Wes said. "It's not the end of the world. Something will turn up."

"It better," Alice said. "And soon, too."

As he had done so many times before, Wes McLain retreated to his basement workshop. On his knees he tried desperately to pray. It was not easy. Jesus, what have I done? Help me. I need your help now more than I've ever needed it. What can I do? Jesus, guide me. Show me the way. Give me strength!

162

7

Marsha Hoyt's bedside phone rang at two-thirty in the morning. Before she could say "hello" the thin, frantic voice of Sam Ott screamed things she could not believe. "Fire, in the kitchen! Smoke is so bad I can't tell!"

For an instant, frozen with shock, Marsha held the phone, heard the background of screams and yelling that drowned out whatever else Sam Ott tried to say. She jumped out of bed, threw on some clothes and ran downstairs. In the hall she dialed Virginia Carver's number. The line was busy. She ran out to her car and headed for the mission.

Marsha raced through the deserted streets and into downtown Rockfort. On Main Street she heard the far-off whine of sirens. It wasn't a dream. It was true. Fire at the mission, Thank God for the sirens. That meant engines were on the way. The fire would be brought under control. Then, as Marsha turned into Mill Street, she saw the frightening yellow glow against low-hanging clouds. How could it be that bad in just a few minutes?

Mill Street was jammed with fire engines and police cars. Marsha pulled off the road, got out of her car and ran. Her way was blocked by fire equipment and hoses. Men in helmets carrying axes ran back and forth. Hundreds of people stood behind police barriers and watched the flames. It looked as if the entire mission building was engulfed. The streams of water seemed to have no effect as flames, cinders and smoke shot fifty feet into the air.

Marsha tried to push her way through the crowd. She had never known such complete desolation. There was nothing she could do, no one to share her grief. It seemed an eternity and then suddenly an arm was around her. It was Jerry Carver. With him were Virginia and Loretta Sims.

"I yelled at the fire chief," Jerry shouted above the noise. "Asked if he knew how it started. He gave me a dirty look."

Marsha told them of Sam Ott's phone call. Sam had also called Virginia. "He must have been asleep in the dorm," Marsha said. "By the time he got downstairs it was probably too late."

Marsha turned to Virginia. They clung to each other.

"All our work. All that money you spent."

"I pray no one is hurt," said Virginia, sobbing.

"Two ambulances are behind the fire trucks," Jerry said. "You can't see very much."

Marsha and Virginia, tears flowing, paced back and forth as if somehow the crowd might part and they could dash through to the mission.

After a while they were joined by Willard Merrill. His anguished lips moved in silent prayer. "It is the work of the devil!" His eyes filled with tears.

By six in the morning the fire had burned itself out. The mission was totally destroyed. The adjoining plant, once the factory itself, had suffered minor damage.

Eighteen persons had been taken to hospitals. Four were pronounced dead. Another six or eight were believed to be missing. No one had an accurate list of those in the mission at the time of the fire. Known to be among the missing was Sam Ott, who had been seen helping the handicapped to get out of the burning building.

8

It was a beautiful morning, a complete change from the blustery November winds of the day before. Judy Brent slept until ten, took a shower, listened to radio reports of the tragic Sin City fire and made a date for tennis at the Country Club at eleven thirty.

She gulped down orange juice, English muffins and coffee, collected her racket and tennis shoes and went out to the garage.

The Brents' garage had room for three cars, Rodney Brent's Continental, a Mercedes 380 SL roadster belonging to Judy and a ten-year-old Jaguar that the banker used for fishing trips to northern Michigan.

Judy went in the side door and automatically flipped the switch to open the large garage door. All three cars were in place. For a moment she was confused. Was it Sunday? Was her father in the den reading the paper? Then she saw it. A length of green garden hose carefully taped to the exhaust pipe and extending along the side of the Jaguar and through the partly open window on the driver's side. She screamed and covered her eyes. Slowly she forced herself to look at her father, slumped over the wheel. She tugged hopelessly at the locked car door, then ran, screaming, out of the garage and didn't stop until she reached the back door of the adjoining estate.

9

News of Rodney Brent's suicide was carried on Rockfort's radio stations at two o'clock. It produced a long line of bank customers intent on removing their funds. The lines continued at drive-in windows until the regular evening closing at eight o'clock. Long before then, the bank was limiting withdrawals to $1,000 per customer.

Early the next morning, bank examiners arrived and officially closed the bank.

At an emergency meeting of the bank's directors and, later, at still another hastily called gathering of the Committee of Fifty, reaction was the same: total shock.

It took the bank's chief loan officer and the treasurer

165

until midnight but they found the answer. Rodney Brent, from his personal account, had made three quarterly interest payments on an overdue loan to Erie H-Tec, Inc., of Cleveland. Total: $990,000.00

Why? One by one the pieces fell into place. A $12 million loan to Erie had been granted without approval of the directors. Buzz Hammond, president of Erie, and Brent were longtime friends. The Wharton School. Brief stints in Washington during the Nixon administration. Together they made a trip to Japan to lure industry to Ohio and Indiana. When Hammond took over at Erie, Brent was on Erie's board. When Erie ran into trouble in 1982, Brent came to the rescue. Now Erie was in default, the company bankrupt.

The bank's directors saw themselves no less guilty than Rodney Brent. They should have known what was going on, but they didn't. Now, their stock in County Trust was worth little or nothing. And depositors' funds were in jeopardy.

In the Brent Room at the City Club, the Committee of Fifty wasted no time in fixing responsibility. Blame for the tragedy had to be assigned immediately, a scapegoat found.

It wasn't Rodney Brent's fault. It was Rockfort. The city was in turmoil. The most prominent real estate lawyer in town took the floor.

"This is the saddest day in the history of our city. Rodney Brent was our dear friend. A friend to each one of us in this room. If just one of us had been with him yesterday, to talk with him, to try to understand what he was thinking, to be helpful and sympathetic, Rodney Brent would be here with us right now.

"Rodney Brent was all right until this mess started in Rockfort. All this nonsense about imitating Jesus is at the heart of our problem! I don't have to tell you what's happened. Businesses failing. Lay-offs! Strikes! Fires! What has diseased this town? What has gripped us by our throats? I'll tell you. A bleeding-heart evangelist! A rabble-rousing preacher! A nosey, meddling disciple of doom! A fire-and-brimstone, wild-eyed maniac! That is our trouble, my friends!"

There were shouts of agreement, a thunder of applause.

"What do we do about it?" an insurance man yelled.

A bedlam of voices cried: "Throw him in jail!" "Bring him to court!" "Get him!" "Burn him out!" The attorney held up his hands, begged for quiet.

"No. We can't use violence. If we do, the law will protect him. It would be a long battle. We couldn't be sure of the outcome. No. We must have him removed from his job."

"How?" they cried. "When?"

"The trustees at the Pleasant Valley Church hired him. The trustees can fire him. We'll make the trustees fire him!"

"Right on!"

"I'd like a committee of three to work with me immediately in getting Merrill ousted."

10

On election night, Willard Merrill was with Roger and Ellen Heath at campaign headquarters. In the tiny store, once a yarn shop, volunteers crowded around a TV set and listened to the returns.

The polls had closed at six. Early returns had the encumbent mayor, Hal Tuttle, running well ahead of Heath. Now the outlying districts of the city began to come in and Heath picked up slightly.

"You see," Ellen Heath said, her eyes alive with excitement, "we're getting into the suburbs with homeowners and more people who care."

"We've a long way to go," her husband observed.

Will Merrill said: "Ellen's right. We never thought we'd carry the inner city. But outside we have a chance."

For an hour their hopes alternately soared and fell. Heath

made gains, appeared to be trimming Tuttle's lead, but at seven o'clock the professor fell off badly.

"We just can't lose!" Ellen said wearily. "How much more to be counted, do you think?"

"Not an awful lot," Heath answered. "This isn't Chicago. It's Rockfort, with about ninety thousand registered voters."

"What we stand for is right," Merrill said. "This city needs you, Roger."

The professor dejectedly studied the tally of votes on a wall chart. "What's right doesn't always win."

By nine o'clock it was all over; Heath had faded. Tuttle, ahead by more than 4,200 votes, was declared the winner.

A television commentator noted: "The strong campaign waged by Hal Tuttle—his budget for broadcast advertising alone came to more than $150,000—was too much for Professor Heath, even though the educator appealed to those most sensitive to crime and corruption in Rockfort."

In a brief announcement for the media, Roger Heath conceded defeat and congratulated Hal Tuttle. One by one, most of the volunteers who had worked together for eight weeks said their sad goodbyes and vowed to win next time.

Merrill, visibly discouraged, tried to console the Heaths and the few helpers who remained. "We can't let this get us down," he said. "My only regret, Roger, is that it took so much of your time and hard work. Some day we will win. Good will triumph. The evil forces in this city will be overcome, as they will be all over the world. We must be patient, and never for a moment give up. That is the only sin. To quit. For when we quit we renounce our faith, our belief. One line from I Timothy 6:12 says it: *Fight the good fight of faith.*

"How can we do less? In Lamentations 3:22-23 we are told *It is of the Lord's mercies that we are not consumed, because his compassions fail not. They are new every morning: great is thy faithfulness.*

168

"That is what we must remember now, always remember in times of defeat.

"Yes, we have lost an election. There will be others. There will be other opportunities. And we will be ready. The Holy Spirit will be with us. We know it. We believe it. In Jeremiah 29:12 we are reminded: *Then shall ye call upon me, and ye shall go and pray unto me, and I will hearken unto you.*"

The minister knelt in prayer and they followed him.

"We need only to accept those four words. I will hear you."

After the others had gone Willard Merrill remained alone amid the clutter of campaign headquarters. His face, now a grim mask of utter discouragement, reflected the agony in his soul. How could he have assumed the election volunteers would still accept his preaching? His blind faith? Had they not seen enough, suffered enough? Rockfort was in chaos. Yet here he was, plunging on, stubbornly insisting his great idea could save the world. Wasn't it time to admit defeat? To give up? To try to repair some of the damage?

The minister, his shoulders slumping dejectedly, made his way slowly to his car.

11

Ann Merrill saw the defeat of Roger Heath as another calamity, one more sorrowful mistake, one more humiliation in her husband's crumbling career. The fire. All those people lost. Including Sam Ott. And now Rodney Brent. Poor man.

Why in heaven's name can't Willard be like other ministers? He has the education, the training. He has the appearance. God only knows, he's attractive enough. Why go completely mad because an unfortunate beggar comes to the door for a handout and later drops dead? Was it Will Merrill's fault?

169

The man was in poor health. Doctor Egbert said so. He didn't just die because he wasn't brought in for a hot meal!

Will Merrill was a wonderful man. She loved him. They had been together for all these happy years. But this business of following Jesus was frightening. It started with a Sunday sermon and now it was a crusade. The city in a mess. People losing jobs. Two physical attacks on Will. The mission burned. Where will it end? Roger Heath for mayor had been doomed from day one. You simply don't drag a wishy-washy teacher out of his classroom and get him elected to the city's top job.

Then there was the other. Will recently had been cold and indifferent in their physical relationship, totally unlike him. He hadn't so much as touched her. Maybe a pat on the shoulder, a routine arm around her waist. That was all. On more than one night in the last two months she had awakened to discover he was sleeping in the guest room. "Had trouble getting to sleep. Didn't want to disturb you," was his explanation mornings when she looked at him questioningly.

Ann sighed. They had always had a good, warm intimacy. Spontaneous and satisfying. Now he was like a stranger. She, too, hadn't slept well in weeks. Couldn't he have been warm and loving just a few times?

Ann Merrill had avoided parishioners. She knew she didn't look her best. She was too distressed to see any of her friends, made all sorts of hastily contrived excuses. She realized she had become irritable, fearful and unhappy.

And now on top of it all had been Janet's alarming call.

Ann entered his study without knocking.

"Janet Lauder called me," she said slowly, firmly. "They're going to remove you. Fire you."

"Who?"

"The trustees, of course. They hired you."

"They won't do that."

"Will, why don't you stop while there's still time? Admit that you're wrong. These people like you in spite of everything but they won't put up with it any longer."

"Because Roger lost?"

"It's more than that. Don't you see? Everything is wrong. That awful fire! Those poor people lost. And look at poor Rodney Brent!"

"Surely they don't blame us for everything?"

"They do, Will! That's what Janet heard. It's all part of the same thing. Reverend Merrill trying to change the world. Live as Jesus would live, you keep shouting. You can't do it, Will! Not in our world. Maybe in some monastery on top of a mountain, but not here. This is Rockfort. Today. Here. Why can't you see that?"

Merrill was silent. He had given his reasons over and over again.

"Do you ever think what this is doing to our marriage?" she asked.

He looked at her. "Ann, I love you, you know that, but..."

"We don't talk to each other. You're so wrapped up in all this you've no time for me." She paused, looked away. "We haven't been together since all this happened. You're like a stranger. You even sleep in another room half the time!"

"I have trouble sleeping."

"You're a good man, Will. I've always loved you. But—I just don't know where all this will end!"

He put his arms around her. For a moment, she seemed to respond and then she pulled away.

"I have nothing more to say," she declared. "I've put a few things in a bag. I'm driving over to Des Moines to visit my sister."

12

Alone in an empty house, Merrill sat in the stillness and went back over five months since the stranger had come to the door. If I'm honest about it, if I'm really truthful, I have to

171

admit that as of today those who have followed me in the program have met only with disaster. Dear Jesus, what have I done to them? To these beautiful souls who have trusted me? Ed Vernon's newspaper up for sale. Wes McLain fired. Don Turner in trouble. The mission burned. Sam Ott, Rodney Brent dead. Roger Heath beaten at the polls.

And now, Ann, my dear wife, has left me.

Merrill rose, clenched his hands and paced in his study. What have I done wrong? My purpose is to help, not harm. I want only to follow You, Jesus. Is that too much to ask? Impossible? I want to do as You would do! But I've failed. I've ruined the lives of my friends. We believed in You, Jesus. Now everything is lost.

Willard Merrill fought back the tears, then he gave up and wept, his body shaken with grief and remorse. After a while he got control of himself and spoke the 23rd Psalm. *The Lord is my shepherd, I shall not want.* The beauty of the words brought tears again. *He restoreth my soul: He leadeth me in the paths of righteousness for His name's sake.* Merrill fell to his knees and continued. *Thou preparest a table before me in the presence of mine enemies: thou anointest my head with oil; my cup runneth over. Surely goodness and mercy shall follow me all the days of my life; and I will dwell in the house of the Lord forever.*

In desperation the minister asked Jesus for help. Show me the way. There is a right way. I have not meant to hurt others, only to follow You, to do as You would do. I cannot blame others for seeing things differently. Bless them. God be with them. But neither can I stand idly by and see sin prevail, the misguided led down paths of evil to destruction.

What does it profit me to have the finest church in the land, the best music, the most affluent congregation, if the forces of the devil run rampant in the land? If children are betrayed? If good people don't accept their responsibilities? If our leaders are incompetent and indifferent? Is it not my job to bring them understanding?

In torment, his face grim, Willard Merrill cried out in despair as he fought to quell the storm within him. His body wracked with pain, his breath coming in short gasps, he gripped the edge of his desk to steady himself. In God's name, what have I done? What misery have I heaped upon my loving friends?

He opened his Bible and the pages were blurred. He shook his head violently as if to dislodge some black web of evil. Staring out at him from the once familiar words was the smiling face of Ann as she had looked so many times over the years. Gradually he was able to focus. Slowly the type sharpened and became clear. *Wherefore take unto you the whole armour of God, that ye may be able to withstand the evil day, and having done all, to stand.* It was Ephesians 6:13. Had he not been standing? Affirming the presence of the Holy Spirit? How could he do more?

Merrill straightened. Somehow he had to go on standing. He had to face evil and adversity. He had to hold fast to his faith, his belief, or all was lost. His wife, his church, his life's work. His life itself.

Abruptly he fell to his knees, head bowed, hands clasped, tears streaming down his face. Dear Jesus, hear my prayers. In this terrible time give me the vision, the energy, the intelligence to do what is right. Isn't it to follow You every step of the way? Can I turn back now? No! I must do as You would do! Live as You would live! Work as You would work! There is no other way for me!

Still kneeling, he repeated over and over again: *Heaven and earth shall pass away but my words shall not pass away.*

As the minister prayed, the power of the Holy Spirit began to descend on him. Serenity crept back to his anguished face. He felt his entire body relax. In his heart there was a spark of new courage, new determination. His eyes became bright and alive. He rose, slowly took a deep breath. Then he forced himself to throw his shoulders back and go to his desk.

On his determined face was resolution, a glow of new-found strength.

13

Early morning phone calls were routine with Arnold Grimsley. He liked to be in his office by seven. Close friends and associates knew they could usually reach him well before the switchboard opened, either on the first trunkline in the system, which was hooked up to ring on his desk, or on his private phone.

"This is Willard Merrill, down in Rockfort," the minister began. "I thank you again for your letter and your very generous check."

"You've had trouble down there. The fire. And I read about Rodney Brent. Too bad. He was popular here in Chicago. Our *Tribune* carried something about the local election. A man named Heath."

"Yes. We hoped he'd do better." There was a pause. "Mr. Grimsley, I'd like to come to Chicago. Would you have a few minutes to see me?"

"I'll make the time."

"When could I come in?"

"Tomorrow?"

"In the morning?"

"Fine."

Arnold Grimsley smiled. Was it coincidence? Mental telepathy? Reverend Merrill and his group of Jesus followers had been on his mind ever since he'd sent off the check. But it had gone beyond that. Arnold Grimsley? Absurd! It was not his style. He was a realist. A fighter. You got what you fought for in this world. And you got it yourself—without anybody's help.

Yet, something had happened to the industrialist. On a recent day, there had been a tough decision to make. A critical decision involving millions of dollars and several thousand employees. He had gone home to mull it over. During his after-dinner coffee he had asked himself: What would Jesus do? He had left the table, laughed to himself and opened his attache case to study the facts in the complex situation. But as the evening wore on, the question had returned: What would Jesus do?

Before going to bed, Arnold Grimsley had made up his mind: he would act from a position of fairness and consideration for the other side. He would go into negotiations tomorrow determined to give as much as he expected to receive.

It had worked. The transaction went smoothly, the deal was a huge success and it was probably going to be very profitable.

From that moment, Arnold Grimsley had become a believer. He prayed. Several times a day. On little things as well as major ones. Always serious, almost dour, he found himself smiling more often. Looking in the mirror in the mornings he saw a new, perky look of confidence when he silently asked: Well, what *would* Jesus do?

More than at any time he could recall, Arnold Grimsley was enjoying himself.

14

Willard Merrill entered the pale green skyscraper on Michigan Boulevard and took an elevator to the thirty-eighth floor. From the start, the two men understood each other. Grimsley, tall, white-haired, trim, his manner sincere and friendly, gave the impression that his visitor was important. You liked Grimsley because he put you at ease. You had his undivided attention.

The minister, Grimsley observed, was open and frank. He had a strong personality. Attractive. You knew he could have been a great success in the world of business.

Merrill explained how his program, based on following Jesus, had resulted in chaos and catastrophe. He told Grimsley about Vernon, McLain, Turner and how these men had sacrificed and failed. He recounted the mission fire.

"Was it set?" Grimsley asked.

"Apparently. To force us out of Sin City, I suppose."

175

"What can I do to help?"

"Rockfort, right now, needs rehabilitation—economic as well as moral," Merrill said. "We have problems with crime, corruption, poverty. But before we can make progress there, we have to improve our situation economically. Especially in Sin City."

Grimsley sat back in his easy chair and glanced out over the lake. When he turned again to the minister, his expression was thoughtful, as if he were looking far into the future.

"Let me think about this," Grimsley said. "Let me see what ideas we might come up with. I'll phone you tomorrow. I'll talk with my people this afternoon."

Merrill rose and thanked him for the meeting.

"Would you mind," Merrill suggested hesitantly, "if we prayed together for a moment? It's a habit with me. Only for a second."

Arnold Grimsley smiled. He took the minister's arm and they knelt together at the edge of a large leather sofa. Merrill asked Jesus to bless their meeting and to bring forth only what might be best for both parties.

Grimsley walked to the elevator with his guest. Then he returned to his desk, he thought back over the weeks. The *Wall Street Journal* story. His letter and check to Merrill. The minister's immediate short note of thanks. Then his visit.

All simple enough. But what had happened to Arnold Grimsley after sixty-four years? He had never been a church-goer. Oh, long ago, to please his mother. But all that was a very long time ago. Since then religion had never entered his mind.

Arnold Grimsley's lips moved almost imperceptively as he thought about Rockfort. What would Jesus do?

15

Back in his study in the afternoon, Willard Merrill tried in vain to control the whirlwind of hopes, doubts and fears that swept through his mind. At three o'clock he endured a visit from two church trustees who gingerly informed him of the Board's displeasure with his conduct in recent months.

The trustees politely but firmly suggested he resign. It would be better all around, they insisted; far preferable to being discharged. If the minister went quietly, they predicted, there would be a minimum of upheaval in the church and everything would soon return to normal.

Merrill listened patiently. He did not argue. But he did not agree to resign, either. He told them he would consider their request; it was agreed to meet in a "few days." Thus Merrill bought time—time he badly needed.

After they left, the minister dwelled on his visit with Arnold Grimsley. The man had been friendly, interested. His "let me think about this" was no routine response. It was not merely a way to end the meeting. Grimsley was kind. His letter, his check, his willingness to see Merrill without delay, were proof enough of the man's sincerity.

Was it, then, too much to hope for? Too much to dream about? Did Merrill have any right, as minister of the Pleasant Valley Church—at least for a few more days—to think that this Chicago industrialist could become concerned about the problems of Rockfort? And actually do something to help?

Willard Merrill knew his own faults. One of them was stubbornness. He rarely gave up on anything worthwhile without a fight. Some preachers, opposed in their idea of following Jesus, would have packed up and run. Bowed to public demand. Caved in to pressure and violence.

But not Merrill.

Through most of the night he prayed that somehow, in some miraculous way, Arnold Grimsley would come through. Why put it down as far-fetched, unrealistic living in a dream world? It was possible.

Where the Holy Spirit is concerned, all things are possible. All doors are open; all channels are clear. Why was it impossible in Rockfort? Willard Merrill prayed for help. He spoke firmly. "Jesus, You guided me to Chicago. You inspired me to make the phone call. Arnold Grimsley agreed to see me. Agreed to consider our problem. Why? He had already sent a check. It was Your guidance, inspiration. Now, will Mr. Grimsley do more?"

The minister prayed for twenty-four hours. He knew he faced the end of his long struggle. The church required his answer. All Rockfort was against him. Business leaders, church-goers, politicians, shopkeepers, the average citizen. Yes, a few loyal supporters remained. And a few impartial church members were sympathetic though they hadn't actually followed him. Why should they? Jesus said that the blind cannot lead the blind.

Willard Merrill wondered how he could have been so blind. He knew that he faced the end of the road and only a miracle could save him.

Exhausted from his long ordeal he idly turned the pages of his Bible, his hands moving mechanically, without direction. For a brief moment he dozed, then awoke to find himself staring at a line in Acts 1:8. *But ye shall receive power after that Holy Ghost is come upon you.* The true meaning of the words, he thought, can only be seen in one way. *I must have faith. Know. Trust. Believe.* He sat in his chair, then suddenly slumped forward on the desk in despair.

I—can't...I can't go on.

At six-thirty in the morning the phone rang.

"Willard. This is Grimsley. I have an idea that may help. Let's talk about it. I'll fly in later today."

If ever there was a time for confident prayer it was now. What could Grimsley have in mind? Will it help? Will it really turn things around in Rockfort, or is it too late? No! It is not too late! It is never too late for Jesus.

With God, all things are possible!

178

Elated, the minister fell to his knees again and lost himself in prayer. He forgot his troubles. He put aside his agonizing doubts, his terrible fear of failure. Only one thought mattered. It will happen! He again opened his Bible and read 1 Corinthians 2:9. *Eye hath not seen, nor ear heard, neither have entered into the heart of man, the things which God hath prepared for them that love Him.*

Slowly, the warmth of the Holy Spirit embraced Willard Merrill.

16

"You've changed my life," Arnold Grimsley said, smiling.

The industrialist was seated in Merrill's study. "Why would it need changing? Most people envy me. All that money! 'If I only had a tenth of what Grimsley has!'"

He laughed. "It's true, Willard, I do have a great deal of money. But how was it accumulated? From being smarter than the next guy? From being lucky? Taking from others? I don't know. Perhaps all three. The point is, I've never really been at peace with myself—until now. Really at peace, contented, proud. There was always tension, irritation, aggravation. Annoyance over little things. Terrible impatience.

"Maybe it's crazy to analyze yourself when you have the material things. Take the money and enjoy yourself. That's the philosophy of many. Do what you can for charity, help whatever good causes appeal to you. And that's it. The rest of the time buy five-hundred-dollar suits, shoes that cost one-fifty. Last week I took ten people to lunch in New York at a restaurant just off Park Avenue. I can't even recall the name of the place. The check was over a thousand dollars. And the food wasn't all that good.

"I guess what I've missed was the peace I've known the last few days. Has it been a week since I wrote to you? Two

179

weeks? It doesn't matter. Thank God you came to see me. I'm glad I'm here in your study right now. I'm more relaxed, happier than I've been in years."

Willard Merrill replied, "Your spirit lightens our problems."

"Let's get into those problems. That's why I'm here. We can't let you fail. Rockfort needs what you're struggling to give. Our country needs you. I had your last two sermons taped. I've listened to them over and over again. You make sense, Willard. Look at the world! Sin. Sorrow. Suffering. Starvation. Homeless people. Crime. Corruption. Terrorists. Fear of nuclear destruction.

"What's the answer? Whatever it is, mankind is not providing it," Grimsley paused and shifted in his chair. "Let me see if I understand you. Tell me if my view of your work is correct.

"The only answer, the one way to save our civilization is through Jesus Christ. Belief in Him. Faith in Him. But more than that. Belief and faith mean little without action. We must start *living* our lives as Jesus would do! That is what He taught! How can we be so shallow as to one moment give lip service to His teachings and then promptly follow the old ways of sin and selfishness?"

"You are right."

"We can't send out a signal or broadcast our message and automatically change the world. We're not that naive. But we must make a start! If only a million people around the world hear us and accept us, we will be on our way. Soon it will be two million. Then ten. The results will provide the momentum. Many will scorn and say 'it's easy enough for Grimsley. What's *he* got to lose? He can live by astrology, palmistry or tea-leaf readings if he chooses to. But I can't!'

"No matter what a person's situation—no matter how bad off he is—he can better his lot if he believes in himself and in Jesus Christ!"

There was a pause. Willard Merrill poured coffee and

placed a cup in front of his guest.

"Here's what we're going to do," Arnold Grimsley continued. "I've kept our vice-president for facilities and services busy since you left my office. We've decided to locate three small manufacturing units here in Rockfort. One plant will lease the old wire and cable shop on West Street. It'll turn out our new support systems for robotics. It's work we've got scattered all over right now. Not very efficient. Then, two smaller facilities will use the old frozen food processing plants in East Rockfort, not far from your mission that was burned out. To begin with, we see perhaps eight or nine hundred jobs. The figure could go to two thousand in eighteen months."

Willard Merrill fought to control his joy. With tears in his eyes, he grasped Grimsley's arm and pressed it in thanksgiving. He was unable to speak.

"This will stimulate Rockfort. Give the city a lift. And we intend to make it clear that Grimsley Industries is coming here as a direct result of the far-seeing, inspiring work of Reverend Willard Merrill. There will be no doubt at all in anyone's mind that you are the driving force. Your ideas are at work. Naturally, we will support your church.

"Our public relations people will issue a press release tomorrow announcing our plans. We don't do things half way. We go all out. And we move fast. I'll have a team down here tomorrow to supervise renovations and design for installation of equipment and to set up hiring procedures. We will have a temporary office until the first facility is operating."

Merrill finally said: "God bless you. The power of Jesus Christ is working in and through you. You will be forever blessed for what you are doing."

The two men knelt together and the minister prayed aloud to Jesus. "Guide us in this wonderful new work. Show us the way. Bless our activities with your love and grace. We are in your hands. Now and forever."

181

The news released by Grimsley Industries electrified Rockfort.

There was rejoicing among workers, excitement among tradespeople. Real estate brokers were enthused. Insurance salesmen, bankers and professional people talked of prosperity of the sort Rockfort had not known since World War II. The *Daily News,* scheduled to cease publication in ten days, ran a banner headline.

$40 MILLION PAYROLL, UP TO 2,000 JOBS
DUE HERE: MERRILL'S WORK CREDITED.

In the *Herald,* the story dominated page one but there was no mention of Reverend Merrill.

GRIMSLEY SELECTS ROCKFORT; INDUSTRY
GIANT WILL HIRE 1,000, USE THREE IDLE PLANTS.

Reactions by various leaders in the community were quoted in both papers.

"This should re-establish Rockfort as a key industrial center." George Weatherbee, attorney.

"Let's hope other companies follow Grimsley's lead. We'll be ready." Elwood McCann, banker.

"Now it's up to Rockfort to deliver." William Dunton, merchant.

"Willard Merrill merits the highest praise." James Evers, President, Lincoln College.

The Committee of Fifty was forced to credit Willard Merrill with helping to bring Grimsley to Rockfort. They couldn't deny Arnold Grimsley's published statements. But in small gatherings at lunch, in the City Club and at the Rockfort Country Club, praise was diluted by skepticism. "How could a minister influence a billion-dollar corporation?" "Do you think this living-as-Jesus idea makes any sense?" "Grimsley's too smart to be taken in by an evangelist." "Who cares? If they hire people and meet their payroll, it's good for all of us."

"This town needs a shot in the arm." "If my business picks up, I'll even go to church on Sunday."

That night, at thousands of dinner tables, the subject was the same. "When will they start up?" "How many jobs?" "What sort of jobs?" "This will be good for Christmas business. People will spend if they see good times ahead."

By evening, telephone usage in Rockfort had reached an all-time high. People called friends and neighbors. Hundreds of long distance calls came from relatives. Those who got through spent only a few minutes talking of the new plants, new employment. The big question became: "How did it happen?" "Is this the work of Jesus?" "Don't be silly! This is the twentieth century." "Yes, but the papers said the company decided after talking with Merrill." "That's nonsense! What does a minister know about big business?" "Grimsley is a follower of Merrill." "They've been broadcasting his sermons. Don't forget that." "You have to admit that Jesus influenced an awful lot of people." "That was two thousand years ago." "His teachings are needed now more than ever." "Maybe, but I don't believe in miracles."

By midnight, the city had quieted down. There was no doubt about its good fortune. Rockfort retired for the night in a thoughtful, optimistic mood. "It sounds good." "Let's wait and see." "How will it affect me?" "Is it the work of Jesus?"

18

Lawrence Butler, vice president of Grimsley Industries, arrived in Rockfort. He was fifty, looking about forty. Short, slim, with good shoulders. Dark hair and piercing brown eyes. He rented an office, hired a secretary and systematically began a series of interviews.

First came Edward Vernon.

"You've made a decision to close the paper. When?"

"The end of the month. Unless we're bought out by Bristol Communications. They've shown interest. But nothing definite."

Lawrence Butler studied a long list of figures. "We'll be running a substantial advertising schedule between now and the end of the year. Institutional ads telling the people of Rockfort what we plan to do and when. Then we'll be describing the skills we'll be seeking, the type of jobs that will be open. Later, we'll announce just when and where applicants may apply. And we'll be announcing the names of Grimsley people like myself who'll be moving here. Not too many. The idea is to hire locally."

He put a preliminary schedule of ads before Vernon.

"Do you think you can continue to publish? We'll need you. We won't be using the other paper right now."

"Mr. Butler," replied Ed Vernon enthusiastically. "We'll keep going!"

Don Turner was next.

"Your second dealership is not entirely closed down. Is that correct?"

"Yes. We have four weeks to go on the contract."

"We'll be needing a small fleet of cars and pickup trucks here but the Rockfort order won't be big enough in itself to keep you open. What we plan to do is buy through you for our plant near Kansas City. That'll be a sizeable order. The vehicles will be shipped direct. You won't even see them. Will there be any problems with the manufacturer?"

"They sell cars. That's all that matters."

"Good. And as a side-line, while you're building your business up again, we'd like you to accept a six-month contract with us to work with Wes McLain in organizing our transportation department here. It's too much for one man at the start. You two can get it running smoothly, then McLain can take over. How does that sound?"

"That will be great!"

In its negotiations, Grimsley Industries was immediately seen as efficient, friendly and honest. There were no blue-sky promises. Leases on the idle properties, with options to purchase, were prepared and signed. Electric, gas, water and other facilities were ordered. A crew was hired to clean up the long-closed buildings. Painters and carpenters were contracted. Within a week, some 100 individuals were already working steadily, and job interviews on a larger scale were scheduled to begin in early January.

The County Trust Company re-opened. After meetings with the Federal Deposit Insurance Corporation, the bank was able to offer sufficient guaranties because of commitments made by Grimsley.

Aware of the city's crime problems, Lawrence Butler, in a meeting with Roger Heath, encouraged the educator to make plans to run again. "Next time, you'll be backed by a strong campaign."

19

Willard Merrill met in his study one afternoon with Marsha Hoyt and Virginia Carver. The two women had just finished serving 540 Thanksgiving meals to the needy in a vacant store in Sin City.

"It was so cramped," Marsha laughed. "I don't know how we did it."

"Our volunteers were wonderful," Virginia said. "They cooked forty-six turkeys, mashed eight bushels of potatoes."

"Janet Lauder alone baked twenty-two apple pies!"

Merrill said: "It was the love of Jesus at work. When I saw all those people lined up—some of them waited hours—and your group standing behind the tables serving them, I knew once and for all that we are on the right course. Everything that's happened in Rockfort in the last two weeks proves to me that it's possible to do as Jesus would do. It is possible to stop, every time we are faced with a decision or an evil thought, and ask ourselves: 'What would Jesus do?'"

Virginia Carver took a notebook from her shoulder purse. "I have a plan. There's an old grinding mill near the river where they used to process grain for wholesalers. I went down there a few days ago. It would take a lot of work but we could use half the place to start."

"A new mission!" Merrill beamed.

"Yes. It's available at a low rental."

Marsha said: "The place could be ready soon on a part-time basis."

"Maybe Grimsley Industries will lend a hand," Merrill said.

"What about you?" Marsha asked, well aware of the minister's ultimatum from church trustees.

"Everything that's happened has quieted them down. After the Grimsley news broke, they phoned. 'We're having a meeting soon,' they said. 'Let everything stand the way it is for another week.'"

Marsha smiled, almost mischievously. "After the fire and everything, the real estate people looked at us strangely when we asked about leasing the old mill. I didn't really know how much to tell them or what to say."

Reverend Merrill smiled and nodded. "It tells you in Luke 12:12: *For the Holy Ghost shall teach you in the same hour what ye ought to say.*

20

The television crew for *60 Minutes* had arrived in Rock-fort two days after the Grimsley story appeared in newspapers. Interviews were filmed with the principals in Willard

Merrill's campaign, including Turner, Vernon and McLain. Marsha Hoyt and Virginia Carver were filmed, telling of their experiences at the mission, against a background of the burned-out ruins. There were taped comments by Lawrence Butler of Grimsley.

The longest interview was with Merrill. He told the story of his program and how it started; he noted the Bible passages supporting his ideas. He frankly revealed the opposition he had met and kept coming back to the loyalty of his dedicated group. At the heart of his comments was the question: What would Jesus do?

The camera crew was allowed to film part of a Sunday sermon at Pleasant Valley Church. Opposition by the trustees faded when one practical trustee noted that contributions had been coming in ever since Merrill's first radio sermon.

"This television show reaches a thousand times more people" he observed. "Why not let them cover us?"

Half way through the filming, the producer of *60 Minutes* discovered that both *Time* and *Newsweek* were in Rockfort on the Merrill story. He decided to rush completion of the program and get it on the air by the time the two news magazines hit the newsstands.

The following Sunday, the *60 Minutes* telecast featured *Can You Live Today as Jesus Did? The Rockfort Story.* It drew overwhelming response. Letters and phone calls poured in. Hundreds of checks payable to Willard Merrill or the Pleasant Valley Church swamped the post-office. A mail room was set up in the Activities Hall at the church and four volunteers began the task of sorting letters and checks and sending out a hastily prepared note of thanks.

Most who wrote expressed their support for Merrill's work. Others asked for more information. Some simply said: "Congratulations" or "Keep up the good work," or "We need what you're teaching."

The church trustees were astounded. Suddenly their

187

church had become one of the most important in the country. Within days, mail from overseas began to come in. The story was the same: congratulations, praise, support, donations, requests for details on how to live as Jesus would live.

Then came a barrage of invitations from churches of various denominations asking Willard Merrill to visit them as a guest minister and deliver a sermon on his mind-awakening beliefs.

21

By week's end, Reverend Merrill was in a state of shock. He could not believe the extent of the reaction. True, he had hoped the television program would help in the drive to turn things around in Rockfort. But never in the world had he expected such an avalanche of enthusiasm. Of one thing he was certain: not everybody was mired in skepticism or tolerant of sin, crime and corruption, or oblivious to the problems of the aged, the poor and the unfortunate. In a material, unbelieving world, millions needed only to be informed, to be guided into new ways of thinking, into living as Jesus would live.

Once they understood, they would act. They would stop and ask themselves: What would Jesus do? Their lives would change. Their circumstances would improve. The world would begin to change. The law of action and reaction as taught by Jesus would be seen as infallible. As it is said in Isaiah 40:31 *they that wait upon the Lord shall renew their strength.*

In his study, Merrill prayed for help. A great victory was at hand. But what of my responsibility? he thought. How am I to make the most of this wonderful opportunity? Jesus, make me worthy of Your trust! Show me the way to be of the greatest help to the most people. Guide me into paths of right action for the benefit of those in need. The sinful, the hungry, the homeless, the aged. Let me give comfort to the unfortunate and encourage hope in those who are desperate and forlorn. Oh Jesus, I ask only to be Thy servant, doing Thy work as Thou would do.

My faith is in You. As in Romans 8:28 *We know that all things work together for good to them that love God, to them who are the called according to his purpose.*

Willard Merrill remained on his knees for a long time, his eyes closed, his mind devoted to prayer, his words centered on Jesus. Never, in all his years as a minister, had he prayed so fervently, so intently. *All my troubles, the problems that seemed so impossible to solve are gathered in now, encircled and erased by Divine love and compassion. They are as nothing in the love of Jesus. I am free then to do one thing: to serve people in need. As Jesus would do.*

At last, in the stillness, the minister became aware of the power of the Holy Spirit. He rose, his face aglow with peace, joy and confidence. He knew beyond all doubt that he would spread the word of Jesus beyond the City of Rockfort, to the entire country and, yes, to the entire world.

22

When Willard Merrill returned home after Wednesday evening service, Ann was in the living room. Without a word they rushed into each other's arms.

They separated and she tilted her head and looked at him with a questioning expression. "I had to come home. Will, can you ever forgive me?"

His smile was tender. "I'm glad. Now everything is in place."

"I love you."

"I love you, Ann."

Her smile was sad. "I could have done so much to help you. All I did was complain and try to change you, and I made things worse for you."

"No."

"Then I ran away. Like a little girl. I'm so ashamed."

He kissed her. "I'm counting on you now. The biggest job is ahead. I need you."

They went into the kitchen and made a pot of fresh coffee while the minister recounted some of the things that had happened.

"Marsha and Virginia are off and running. They have an old mill and their new mission opens this week. Jerry Carver's working with them. They have plans to open other missions. One of the nicest things is that Loretta Sims has a full-time job with them. She's the former call girl who was one of the first saved at the old mission."

He smiled and shook his head. "It's beyond my wildest dreams. The television show, all the publicity. And television may produce an extra dividend. The producer apparently is quite taken with Virginia Carver. He flew back twice last week to take her to dinner."

December

1

Don Turner phoned Ed Vernon and they met for lunch at the City Club. "I thought I'd better give you this one in person," Turner said casually. "I'm starting a new ad schedule with you this week. Grimsley's 40-vehicle fleet order for Kansas City hit Detroit like a hurricane. They renewed my franchise for three years. We'll be back in the old location next month."

"Congratulations."

"What about you?"

Ed Vernon smiled. "Oddly enough, quite a few of Rockfort's biggest advertisers decided they couldn't do without us. We have more business booked now than when all the trouble began. And circulation is climbing back up."

"You're not running racing results, crime stories, violence and all the rest?"

"No. But we must be doing something right." He raised a hand to signal the next item. "Dana Bell's coming back. He told the *Herald* he was sorry but he'd made a mistake."

2

In Mayor Hall Tuttle's office at City Hall, a special meeting of the mayor's cronies on the city council was in progress. Tuttle, a square, sturdy man with a round smiling face, aimed a pencil at the group. "There's something starting here. This

191

Grimsley outfit's not fooling. They intend to back Heath for council next year. If he wins, one of you'd be out. This Merrill and his do-gooders are getting strong."

He paused to light a cigarette. "There's a big push coming in Rockfort. We can count on it. These reformers, they'll be sticking their noses into a lot of places."

The council members stared blankly.

"We can't wait for the crusaders to run over us," Tuttle went on. He consulted a scrap of paper on his desk.

"I want you to go into session and come out with three new bills. One. Make it unlawful to operate an adult bookstore in Rockfort. They peddle sex like it was potato chips. It's like rotten hatred against women and children. Close 'em down." Tuttle rose and stood behind his chair. "Two. No more 'happy hours'. They serve only one drink at a time, no reduced prices. Three. We move all bars from three o'clock closing back to one o'clock. Even that's too late but you got to give them some room."

The president of the council spoke. "What about Sin City?"

"Take it easy. Don't push too fast. Get these three bills shaped up right away. The police will put the pressure on Sin City. Get tough with the drug dealers and porno people and the under-the-counter liquor dealers. They'll make a bunch of arrests. People'll think we're *all* members of Merrill's church. Make this stick and this town'll be a model. Next time teevee comes to town I want to be on it."

3

Willard and Ann Merrill had finished dinner when the doorbell rang. It was Marsha Hoyt with Jerry Carver. Marsha was too excited to sit down.

"We wanted you to be the first to know," she said glowingly. "Jerry and I are engaged!"

The minister said: "God be with you. Wonderful news!"

Marsha tossed her auburn hair back in an ecstatic gesture and gave Jerry an adoring, happy look. "He's working with us every day. Full time. He said he'd do it even if I weren't there!"

"He's a fibber," Merrill said laughingly.

Marsha's smile was joyous. "I told him I was the boss. He can't quit his job now no matter what happens."

When the couple had gone, Merrill took his wife in his arms. "She's very happy."

She snuggled close to him. "Not any happier than I am."

They went into the study. Merrill grasped her hand and they knelt in prayer. He felt closer to his wife than at any time in their marriage. He knew that no matter what happened nothing would separate them ever again.

He spoke softly, calmly. "We thank Jesus for our wonderful relationship. For our marriage. Our work together. We go forward together now in ever greater opportunities to serve, to live as He would live."

4

On Saturday, at five in the afternoon, Ann Merrill rushed into the house carrying a brown envelope. She beamed at her husband. "I didn't think it would take so long. I went through hundreds of letters in Activities. Then at the *News*, Ed Vernon called in a young reporter to help and we went over all the wire service material since the Grimsley announcement and the *60 Minutes* program."

He looked at her questioningly.

"It's incredible," she continued. "From all over the country, even from abroad." She took a batch of typed pages from the envelope.

193

"All these wonderful things are happening to people." She smiled happily. "Promise me, Will, you'll read this list to the congregation tomorrow at the end of your sermon."

"All right."

He looked at the material, smiled. Then he put his arms around his wife and kissed her.

5

The next morning the Pleasant Valley Church was jammed. An overflow crowd filled Activities. For the first time, a major radio and a television network covered the sermon. Willard Merrill offered thanks to the many individuals and organizations that had joined in supporting the program. His remarks ended with a plea. "Believe in Jesus. Follow Him. Take up your Cross. Seek the comfort of the Holy Spirit. Pray that you may live life as He would. Start and end each day by asking, what would Jesus do? Only in this way will you—and the world—be saved from sin, from annihilation."

The congregation waited. "My dear wife," he said quietly, "spent most of yesterday rounding up some items that appeared in the press and over the air in the last week or so. Also, excerpts from a few of the many letters we've received. We want you to hear some of them.

"...*a woman in Darien, Connecticut.* I used to spend all my time playing golf and bridge. Then I asked myself, would Jesus do this? I've become a hospital volunteer."

"...*a young girl in Atlanta, Georgia:* Jesus would never be as selfish as I've been. Now, every day after school I do what I can for an old lady next door."

"...*a young minister near Tulsa, Oklahoma:* I had decided to give up. Just couldn't make ends meet. Would Jesus do that? No. I'm going on no matter what."

194

"...*a merchant in Syracuse, New York:* I was about to divorce my wife. I asked myself if Jesus would do this. Soon I realized it was mostly my fault, not hers. We're together again."

"...*a welfare recipient in New York:* One day I found a wallet in the street. I could've used the money. I don't have anything. What would Jesus do? I found the owner, returned the money."

Willard Merrill paused and looked with pride at Ann, seated in the first pew, and then went on.

"*Detroit News:* Three daily newspapers in the state, apparently reacting to the influence of the Reverend Willard Merrill have all but eliminated stories about violence."

"*Kansas City Star:* A car dealer in Topeka erected a sign in his showroom reading 'Yes, Jesus would buy a car here. We live as He would live."

"*Miami Herald:* A developer told this newspaper his new multi-million dollar rehabilitation project in one of the city's worst slum areas is based on doing what Jesus would do."

"I have dozens of others here, all equally inspiring," Merrill said. "We ran the list off on our Xerox. Copies will be available for you on your way out."

The next issue of *Time Magazine* carried its own roundup of items:

...Senator B.D. David (D.Ga.) had one of Merrill's sermons inserted into the Congressional Record. Before a packed Chamber he urged his colleagues to ask, What would Jesus do? before making decisions.

...a Russian delegate to the United Nations this week sought asylum in the U.S., vowing to devote his life to working for peace. He said he was inspired by the thought: What would Jesus do?

...when a wealthy Brazilian banker caught a Merrill sermon via satellite, he announced he was giving four-fifths of his fortune, estimated at $200 million, to aid the poor. ...a White House source said the First Lady stopped the President one morning before an important meeting and said: "Don't forget to ask, What would Jesus do?"

...reliable sources insist that after the daughter of a high ranking official at the Kremlin asked her father to consider living as Jesus would live, the dignitary appeared unusually thoughtful as he headed for a session with the Politburo.

...Wealthy industrialist Arnold Grimsley formed an organization made up of the CEO's of most of the Fortune 500 Companies. Its objective: to do business according to the teachings of Jesus.

6

Demand for Willard Merrill as a guest minister skyrocketed. He made a quick trip to speak at an overflowing audience at Los Angeles' largest auditorium and appeared before a capacity crowd at New York's Madison Square Garden.

The minister seemed to grow in wisdom and strength as he spoke movingly of daily problems in terms of Jesus' teachings. Wherever he preached, his messages were relevant, provocative:

"...Everyday the news reports more suicides by the young. What a tragedy! The taking of a precious, God-given life, before it's even begun. Why? Society cries for an answer. And the answer is obvious. The absence of God in their lives—no Jesus to guide them. The result is that life has no meaning. Life only has meaning when it's lived according to Jesus."

"...What's going on? Boys and girls living together out of

wed-lock. Wives cheating on their husbands. Husbands cheating on their wives. Abortions increasing. Unmarried pregnant girls. Jesus never meant us to live this way! Such sinning can only lead to sadness, misery. Only in Jesus can we find happiness, joy, peace. The Beauty of the Good Life! Pray that more people will find it!"

"...The Family! Dear God what is happening to The Family? Husbands and wives living apart. Children living apart from Mothers and Fathers. God created the Family as the foundation of Society. When it goes society disintegrates. History proves it. Pray for The Family. Pray that more people will come to accept the beauty, the joy of The Family!"

"...We're sinning more, and realizing it less. That's what a great psychologist tells us. And it's true. Notice how easy it is to tell a lie? Nothing to it. In the highest echelons of governments the lie is a way of life. But the easy lie often leads to other bigger lies. And they often lead to bigger sins—crimes against man, against society. Sin begets sin. Don't start with the easy lie. Sin is infectious!"

"...Pornography in movies, magazines, books. In television—right in our homes. And now—child pornography. The vilest sin of all! Where will it end? It will either end in a decadent society, or in a wholesome society that lives by the teaching of Jesus. The choice is ours."

"...Mind your own business! Preach the Bible in church! Stay out of our affairs! That's what many have told me. Well, I was called to teach the word of God. I have the responsibility to speak out against what is evil, based on the Bible. To preach the teachings of Jesus. To concern myself with moral and ethical values. I will not confine my preachings to the four walls of my church! I will preach the word of God to all who will hear me! That is my mission in life."

His manner was honest and forthright. His subjects relevant to today's problems, the message easy to understand. Speaking requests mounted. Soon, the minister—always accom-

197

panied by Ann—was spending most of his time flying from pulpit to pulpit, arena to arena. In his wake, Followers of Jesus groups sprung up and grew in influence.

But Rockfort remained his home, and The Committee of Fifty proudly bought and donated land in Sin City for a new Willard Merrill Community Center to aid the needy.

7

Willard Merrill sat alone in his study, his thoughts leaping years ahead to a time when his dreams for the world would be true and real for all to see.

He saw Marsha and Virginia and Jerry and Loretta Sims opening missions for the poor and homeless and sponsoring new rehabilitation centers for alcoholics and drug users.

The minister saw Ed Vernon's paper grow to a national, then an international, Christian daily.

He saw Don Turner and Wes McLain in demand as speakers before groups to explain how it is possible to conduct business the way Jesus would.

He pictured Roger Heath in a key role in Washington, influencing other lawmakers to live as Jesus would live.

Merrill's determined vision was one in which inspired millions everywhere were joyously living their lives free of sin, alcohol, drugs. They were actively reaching out to help the less fortunate, working for decency, honesty and a world at peace.

Was it too much to expect? No. Not at all. If people in all lands lived as Jesus would live, doing as He would do, it would happen. It would be the work of the Holy Spirit.

When? How long? he asked himself. There has been great progress—but so much is still to be done.

Willard Merrill fell to his knees and prayed aloud. Dear Jesus, it is all there waiting to happen. Your truth and love is waiting to shine upon us all. It is what You have told us to expect. Help us make it happen! We abide by, believe in, the beauty of the 37th Psalm. *Trust in the Lord, and do good... Commit thy way unto the Lord; trust also in him; and ye shall bring it to pass. And he shall bring forth thy righteousness as the light, and thy judgement as the noonday. Rest in the Lord, and wait patiently for him...*

EPILOGUE

On the first anniversary of Reverend Merrill's appeal to his parishioners to join with him in following Jesus, a special service was held at the Pleasant Valley Church. The program opened with a silent prayer for the stranger whose dramatic appearance had stunned the congregation on that memorable Sunday. The minister's sermon followed; it was inspiring as it recounted the year's events and heralded glorious accomplishments to come. The service closed with a solo by Marsha Hoyt. It was the first rendition anywhere of a new song written by Marsha Hoyt Carver.

The Day Jesus Came to Our Town
We were a sinning people—
Crime, greed, hate and adultery
—Far away from the teachings of Jesus
And then everything changed
—The Day Jesus Came to Our Town
People became real brothers
Concerned about their neighbors
Love replaced hate, Goodness replaced sin
The Day Jesus Came to Our Town

The Day Jesus Came to Our Town
I found you
The Day Jesus Came to Our Town
My life changed
Peace and love
Joy and happiness
Were mine
The Day Jesus Came to Our Town.